THE TRUTH ABOUT
REFERRALS
FROM PATIENTS & DENTISTS

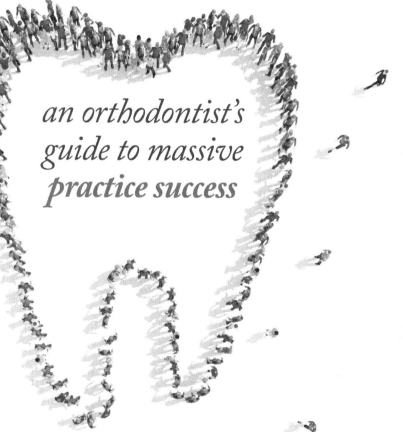

an orthodontist's guide to massive practice success

DUSTIN S. BURLESON, DDS

The Truth About Referrals from Patients and Dentists

Cover Design and Interior Layout: Jeff & Joy Miller | FiveJsDesign.com

Cover image: Shutterstock—*tai11*
Icons made by Freepik from *www.flaticon.com*

CONTENTS

INTRODUCTION: Why Referrals Are So Important 1

PART I: THE TOP FIVE REASONS
PATIENTS AND DENTISTS DON'T REFER

CHAPTER ONE: Reason #1: Apparent Busyness
They Don't Refer Because They Assume You Are Busy Enough 9

CHAPTER TWO: Reason #2: Inadequate Know-How
They Don't Refer Because They Don't Know How Or Don't Have Adequate Tools . . 17

CHAPTER THREE: Reason #3: Lackluster Service
They Don't Refer Because Their Experience With Your
Practice Is Adequate Or Sufficient, But Not Extraordinary. 29

CHAPTER FOUR: Reason #4: Ordinary Welcome
They Don't Refer Because They Are Not Welcomed To Your Practice In A BIG Way. 41

Chapter Five: Reason #5: Inadequate Thanks
They Don't Refer Because They Are Not Thanked Adequately And Promptly. . . 53

PART II: PRACTICAL STRATEGIES FOR BUILDING
YOUR PROFESSIONAL REFERRAL SYSTEM

CHAPTER SIX: Getting Started
Why Most Small Businesses Don't Have A Referral
System In Place And How You Can Do The Opposite 67

CHAPTER SEVEN: The Top 10 Strategies Used to Encourage Referrals
What To Send And How To Send It 79

CHAPTER EIGHT: Timing and Referral Strategy
When To Thank For Referrals And When To Ask For More. 91

CHAPTER NINE:
How To Use The Referral System To Put Your Internal Marketing On Autopilot. . 103

CHAPTER TEN:
Key Metrics And Performance Indicators For Rapid Practice Success. 115

CHAPTER ELEVEN:
Why Most Doctors Don't Adequately Think Through
Their Referral System And What You Can Do About It. 127

CHAPTER TWELVE:
Working With Referring Dentists. 139

CHAPTER THIRTEEN:
Working With Referring Physicians 149

CHAPTER FOURTEEN:
Working With Referring Medical Specialists. 161

CHAPTER FIFTEEN:
Working With Other Small Business Owners, Medical Spas,
Health Fairs, And Community Events 173

CHAPTER SIXTEEN:
The Big Event—How To Use Events For More Referrals 185

CHAPTER SEVENTEEN:
Employee Delegation And Referral System Responsibilities. 195

CHAPTER EIGHTEEN:
Employee Incentives With A Focus On Mastery, Autonomy, And Purpose 207

CHAPTER NINETEEN:
Local Nonprofit Or Charity Programs And
Establishing Your Compelling Reason Why. 219

CHAPTER TWENTY:
Everyone Is In The Referral Business. 231

INTRODUCTION
WHY REFERRALS ARE SO IMPORTANT

BY PICKING UP THIS BOOK, YOU HAVE ALREADY TAKEN A HUGE STEP TOWARD GETTING MORE referrals for your business. Realizing that you *need* more referrals is the first step on the path to actually getting more of them. The problem I have found with the many practices I have worked with is that most dentists and orthodontists do not truly understand referrals. Sure, they know they need referrals and they do get them sometimes, but that is where their knowledge of the issue both begins and ends.

But you can do better than that. In fact, you *must* do better if you want to grow your practice to the level of success you have been dreaming of.

In case you haven't figured it out yet, referrals are essentially like gold in the dental field: they are highly valued and desired by everyone. You just need to know how to get them in order to tap into the wealth of business they can and will bring to your practice.

Most practices I have worked with have no idea if their patients are referring them or not. And if their patients are *not* referring, they rarely know the reason why. Without this information, it's impossible to know what is or isn't working in your practice. Referrals are a gold mine that you need to tap into, and you can only do so by understanding the information and putting it into action.

Through dental and individual referrals, you are going to be opening your doors to patients who are both in need of and ready for your services. If you are not getting the patient and dental referrals you would like—or you don't know if you are—it's time to put some serious time and energy into changing this. Referrals are a proven way to grow your practice.

WHAT ARE REFERRALS?

Over the years, I've spoken with many people who own and run their own orthodontic or dental practices. I've come to realize that a common thread among all of us is that we often don't identify what referrals really are, and we rarely ever name them as such. We use a variety of words to describe what really boils down to being a referral. You will commonly hear people talk about word-of-mouth recommendations or reviews, but you rarely hear them identified as what they really are—*referrals.*

These word-of-mouth recommendations *are* your referrals. Perhaps you haven't been identifying and tracking them as such until this point, but that's what they are. These word-of-mouth referrals may come your way through a friend, an online review, your marketing piece handed off to someone else, another doctor, or even a coworker. There is no limit to the number of places the word-of-mouth recommendations can come from, but they all add up to being referrals. The more you know about where the referrals are coming from and how you are getting them, the bigger impact they can have on your growth. In order to have an effective referral system, it is important that you know who your referrers are, make the right tools available to make it easier for them to refer you, and track where your referrals come from. When you have this information and a system in place, you will feel confident and comfortable; and you will reap the benefits of a continuous influx of new patients.

> Most practices I have worked with have no idea if their patients are referring them or not. And if their patients are **not** referring, they rarely know the reason why.

Chances are, referrals have been your best source of getting new patients all along; but if you are like most doctors, you just didn't realize it. Your unplanned referral system has been quietly working in the background, getting you referrals from a variety of sources, but you didn't realize how powerful it was—or that it *could* and *should* be powerful.

Now that you are going to harness the power of that referral system and take control of it, you will see clearly just how powerful it really is and what it can do for your business. Once your referral system is in place, you will no longer overlook how vital it is to your practice.

REFERRALS AND THE RETURN ON INVESTMENT

One thing that doctors have concerns about when it comes to creating a referral system is being able to track their return on investment (ROI). For the most part, it's common knowledge that you should know if you are getting a good ROI for your efforts when it comes to advertising, marketing, and public relations. But if you are focusing *all* your efforts on tracking the ROI for advertising, marketing, and public relations, you are missing a large part of the equation—your referrals. Sure, you can keep track of how much money you spend by advertising or sending out a special marketing message through traditional mail. But where people get a little confused is how you track the ROI for a referral system.

If your efforts have been going toward putting money into advertising, direct mail, and promotions, then you may feel comfortable because you have something you can track. You can even create a spreadsheet and see how much was spent and how many people responded, letting you know exactly what your ROI was. It's a little different when it comes to a referral system—but different in a great way.

A referral system is going to lower your costs, so you will not have to spend as much money advertising and marketing your office. Your costs are now going to include things like having the right marketing tools on hand to give out, keeping a stash of gift cards on hand to surprise your patients with, and throwing little after-office parties and events. The numbers you create are not going to be as clear-cut as they would be for placing an advertisement and tracking how many people respond to it. But referrals will bring you far more quality, new patients and will cost you much less in the long run.

A mother once told me a story about a pediatrician who advertised everywhere in her county. She would see his office in magazines, newspapers, and even on billboards. The pediatrician was paying to have his name plastered everywhere. New to the area, one day her son needed to see a pediatrician for a spider bite he had gotten on his leg. She hadn't yet lined up a pediatrician, but remembered seeing his office name all over the place, so she gave them a call and got an appointment.

Unfortunately, the doctor had such poor customer service that for her it was one and done; she did not want to go back there a second time. Had this doctor provided better service, he would have maintained a new patient. Had he provided service that was above and beyond, he would not only have maintained that new patient, but he would have likely gotten referrals out of it—and he would have *saved* money because he wouldn't have had to spend so much in advertising his office. That pediatrician had to continuously spend a lot of money on advertising simply because he wasn't providing the type of patient service he should have been. It was costing him far more than he will ever know.

Meanwhile, his competition down the road was a pediatrician who was so busy she had to turn new patients away. Word-of-mouth advertising—which is referrals—had sent more people than she could accommodate, but she was aware of her capacity and strove to maintain it and keep everyone comfortable.

MAKING REFERRALS YOUR FIRST PRIORITY

You are not alone if your referral system needs some help. Most practices are busy focusing on their advertising, marketing, and public relations, so they let the chips fall where they may when it comes to referrals. They continue to get *some* referrals—they may chalk it up to word-of-mouth from one person or another—but they haven't done anything more organized to encourage them.

Until this point, your top priorities have likely rested with advertising and marketing or management and clinical care. But you can save a lot of money and get more business by making a good referral system your top priority—and you don't have to sacrifice clinical care to do it.

In our profession, we've been led to believe that high volume correlates with poor quality. But there's not a single published study that supports that premise. In fact, there are hundreds of medical outcomes articles that show exactly the opposite. You can welcome more new patients into your practice, and the most efficient way to do that is to increase the number of referrals to your office.

If something is happening by accident in your practice—like referrals who show up without any system in place—then you can make the same thing happen *on purpose* with the right strategy. When it comes down to it, we need to remember that the customer is in control—or the patient in our case. When we provide service to them that goes above and beyond and surprises them with its quality, we stand out in their mind. When we are anything but boring, they want to talk about us and share their experience with others.

Patients are the driving force and are in control. But there are things we can do to help steer that energy, work to leverage the power of it, and ensure that our message is consistent. When we do that, our practices will flourish.

Having an effective referral system in place is crucial to the growth and success of your practice. With that in mind, I've uncovered what I think are the top five reasons that patients and dentists *don't* refer. These five reasons are ones I have discovered through my own experience, by asking others about their experience with referrals, and through helping numerous others in their practices. I've seen the process firsthand, I've inquired about it, and I've taken it under serious consideration.

Throughout the first section of this book, I will be sharing these top five reasons with you. Hopefully, this will help you identify why you might not be getting the dentist referrals you would like to have, and *need* to have, in order to take your practice to the next level.

With each chapter, you will come one step closer to making it happen. Once that effective referral system is in place, you will wonder how you ever managed without it.

PART I

THE TOP FIVE REASONS PATIENTS AND DENTISTS DON'T REFER

REASON #1: APPARENT BUSYNESS— THEY DON'T REFER BECAUSE THEY ASSUME YOU ARE BUSY ENOUGH

BELIEVE IT OR NOT, THIS IS THE SINGLE BIGGEST REASON WHY PEOPLE DON'T SEND REFERRALS your way. This may be hard to believe at first because you assume that your patients have no idea how busy—or not busy—your office really is. While that may be technically true, there are many subtle clues your patients perceive on a regular basis that help them form their opinion about how busy your office is. These clues you inadvertently reveal to your patients are far more important than you probably realize.

Think about the last time you were speaking with a patient or a dentist who may be able to send you some referrals. In all likelihood, this took place when you were already slammed with patients. You may have been busy between patients, running from one room to the next and, well, you probably looked really busy.

That's how most people see us. They see us only when we are really busy. They probably aren't going to walk into our office and find us with our feet propped up on the desk, twiddling our thumbs, and wondering when our next patient will arrive. That's just not how it happens. What actually happens is that people see you only in a state of busyness, so they assume you are already busy enough in your practice. Consequently, they don't bother to refer your office to anyone else.

THE PROBLEM WITH YOUR PERCEIVED IMAGE

If you are like most other doctors in our field, the only time you see patients or other dentists is when you are doing work-related tasks of some sort. Rarely do we doctors see these people in environments that are relaxed, that give us an opportunity to interact with them in a less formal manner.

But the good news is that you *can* change this, and you absolutely should. You want your patients and other dentists to see you at patient appreciation parties or hosting a continuing education event in your office where you invite area dentists and hygienists. When you do this, you open yourself up to showing them another side of you, letting them get to know you and providing the opportunity to mingle. That's where relationships begin; and when that happens, the referrals will soon follow.

When people feel that your office is already busy enough, they tend to be more reluctant to give a referral. If they learn the person they referred didn't have a good experience, it's their own reputation on the line. When people make referrals, they want the person they refer to be happy with their experience. If they perceive you are too busy already, they will likely assume that you will also be too busy to offer the people they refer to you the quality of care they deserve. They assume that it will be difficult to get an appointment, that you will be rushed during their care, and that the whole experience will be a bust. They also expect the person they referred will then inform them that their experience didn't live up to the hype because you were too busy. To put it plainly, they assume that others won't have a good experience at your already-too-busy office, so they just keep mum or refer others to someone else entirely whom they feel is probably less busy.

THE PROBLEM WITH SPLITTING YOUR ATTENTION

Here is another fear that many of your patients have. If they see your office is already busy enough, they believe it may become increasingly difficult to get enough of your attention for themselves. Consequently, the last thing they want to do is refer even more people to your already busy office, because if your office can't handle the increased patient load, then they themselves might get put on the back burner. In other words, they fear that if they refer more and more friends, you will have less and less time available for their own treatment.

When it comes down to it, **many of your patients actually prefer to keep you as their own little secret.** They love you and your office, but they want you all to themselves. They don't want to share you and your office with anyone else, and especially not with several of their friends they could refer your way.

Chances are, there are a few businesses that *you* like having all to yourself as well. Have you ever been to a brand new restaurant or an exclusive resort, and you loved it? You initially shared your excitement with everyone, wanting people know how great this new place was. Your friends all started flocking there, and in turn *they* also started telling others about it. The news of this great place spread like wildfire from one person to the next. Then it became everyone's hot spot, rather than just yours.

As it became more and more popular, you started wishing you had never told people about the place. You want your little secret place back, because now it's always busy, it's hard to get a table, and it's bustling with people rather than being that quiet place you fell in love with. Spreading the message about this new place removed the allure for you.

> **!**
>
> *When people feel that your office is already busy enough, they tend to be more reluctant to give a referral.*

Your patients are no different. Right now they have you and your office all to themselves; and what some of them fear is that if they spread the news about it, they will regret it. They like it just the way it is now, and they don't want it to become really busy and for it to change if too many others they refer start going there as well. They want to keep it their little secret.

Between not wanting to share your place with anyone else and assuming your office is already busy enough, you are losing out on the power of all the referrals they could be sending your way.

THE PROBLEM OF DWINDLING SERVICE

I have personal experience with this exact situation of dwindling service. Years ago I found what I thought was one of the best-hidden gems. It was an Italian restaurant in a neighborhood that was still considered to be "up-and-coming." This was the type of restaurant where the chef would come out and interact with the customers, the servers all knew you by name, and they even knew your favorite dishes and the way you preferred things. They offered meals that were a great value, even having a wine list that was both diverse and reasonably priced.

But more importantly, the food there was unbelievably delicious. The atmosphere was unique and inviting, and the place was never empty—but it also wasn't packed either. In other words, we could always get in and expect a great meal and service.

I was always content to keep this little place to myself and let it be "my little secret." The restaurant seemed busy enough to me, and I didn't want to share my favorite new place with anyone else. But not everyone felt the same way about keeping quiet about how great this place was. Word got out—and in a big way.

It became increasingly busy as more people spread the message about this wonderful little restaurant. Within just a few months, everything changed. The place became packed on a regular basis. And with this increased busyness, the service—and even the food—suffered. The restaurant seemed to struggle handling the increased demand.

When businesses experience a marked increase in customers, they have to make changes to accommodate the higher volume of business. Those businesses that play their cards right will end up growing and thriving; but others who don't know what to do with that newfound success will need to make some tough decisions.

> When businesses experience a marked increase in customers, they have to make changes to accommodate the higher volume of business.

For the Italian restaurant to have handled the capacity problem it was facing, it would either have had to expand to accommodate the number of people it could comfortably serve, or it would have had to raise the prices in order to serve only those willing to pay extra for the high quality service and food.

In all honesty, I would have been one of those people who would have gladly paid more money to keep things as they were when I first came to love this restaurant. Paying the premium would have been worth it to me, because I enjoyed the food and restaurant so much.

This small restaurant, however, wasn't very business savvy. The decisions the owners made didn't improve their ability to serve the volume of customers they were getting. And as a result, everything I loved about this restaurant began to suffer. In less than a year, one of my favorite Italian restaurants became a place that I simply wouldn't go to, and it was certainly not a restaurant I would recommend to others. The owners were too busy for their operational systems, and they didn't make the right decisions to help them absorb that increased burden and grow their business from it.

Just like me, many of your patients have had their own similar experiences. They have referred people somewhere or mentioned how great a place it was, only to watch that business go downhill once it got really busy. They regretted sharing that information about their "little secret" and now they feel the same way about your business. Many of your patients fear that if they let others know about your office, it will become busier with a decline in the quality of service they currently receive.

HOW TO LOOK LESS BUSY

Your patients pay attention to what's going on in your office when they call to make an appointment or come in for one. If all they ever see or hear is that you are busy and running around like crazy, they assume you are busy enough. Nobody needs more business sent their way when they are that busy. This is why it is important that you provide opportunities for them to see you in a different light, ones where they see you relaxed, smiling, and happy.

There are many ways that you can do this, including something as simple as holding a patient appreciation party at your local movie theater, roller skating rink, amusement park, or water park. By doing so, you will let everyone see you in a more relaxed environment; and it will serve as a reminder to them that your business is built on referrals from existing patients. You want to give them a reason to refer you, and this is a major step in the right direction.

Make it your goal to stop letting your patients only see you as someone who is too busy. If that's the only way they see you, then you are going to have a difficult time growing your business. It is crucial that they see you outside the office, so they see that you are not running in five different directions with your hair on fire. When you give them opportunities to see and speak to you *outside* the office, you will show them you are relaxed and able to take on more patients; and you will help strengthen ties with them—which will also make them want to refer you more often.

> Your patients pay attention . . . If all they ever see or hear is that you are busy and running around like crazy, they assume you are busy enough. Nobody needs more business sent their way when they are that busy.

Start making a list right now of the various ways you can let your patients see you outside of the office. Consider some of the events you can plan and invite people to, and the ones that someone else is having that you are invited to which you can attend. Look for events that get you in a more relaxed environment with dentists, hygienists, and the community.

There are many ways you can do this: you can host events yourself or attend community events or those hosted by others. Look for several community events per year where you can mingle with people and show them your fun side. If you like sports, consider joining an adult sports team or helping coach some kids. The more you get out there and show people another side of you, the better off you will be.

HOW TO MAINTAIN QUALITY SERVICE

Your patients may fear your service will dwindle if too many others find out about your office, so focus on not letting that happen. To avoid such problems, identify capacity factors and maintain a comfortable capacity within your practice. In fact, it's *essential* to make sure you are paying attention to capacity issues at your practice; or the work you do to set up a referral system will be largely wasted.

Expand Your Office Space

If capacity becomes a problem you don't address, it could have an enormously negative impact on your business, which is the opposite of what you are trying to achieve. If you outgrow your space, it is worth it to invest in expanding so you can better accommodate your patients and maintain a comfortable atmosphere. Unlike the restaurant story I shared, you can make smarter decisions and be better equipped to adapt to capacity issues as your business grows.

Expand Your Business Hours

In your practice, you get to decide when you are open for business, including setting your schedule for Fridays, Saturdays, and evenings. You don't want your new patients to ask for a 4 p.m. time slot and then tell them it's going to be three to four weeks before you can get them in. That tells them you are busy enough and you are not very eager about making them a new patient. That's not the right message you want to send to them.

Adjust Your Pricing

Make paying attention to capacity issues a priority, and when you become too busy for your current office, either expand your office space or hours so that you can meet those demands, or raise your prices. When you raise your prices you will be losing some of the volume, but your practice will still be making more per year. Those who love your service will be willing to pay the extra to keep it more exclusive and open to them, just as I would have happily done with my favorite little Italian restaurant.

Don't shy away from raising your prices when you reach capacity. It's not a sin to make a profit, and you should strive to do just that. Rolls Royce and Bentley are not about to start making more cars when the demand for their vehicles goes up. Rather, they make as many as they can using their quality standards that they have had in place for over one hundred years; and they just raise their prices.

Likewise, Disney announced price increases for its theme parks six times within the last four years. It would be very difficult for Disney theme parks to add to their capacity, especially since new hotels and attractions take years to complete. Yet they continue to get people to pack the place despite the repeated price increases. That's because they have made the decision to weed out those who won't pay the additional price, and still provide the happiest place on Earth for those who can and will. They make over $2 billion in profits from their theme parks annually, and nobody feels bad about it. You shouldn't either. While you may want to help people have the best smile they can have, you are also an entrepreneur who wants to make a healthy profit. There's nothing wrong with that, and I hope you take the necessary steps to make it happen.

The bottom line is that the only way to ensure you are providing a quality service to your patients as you grow is to pay attention to capacity and then set your fees appropriately. The customers who stick with you will appreciate what you have done because they know they are still receiving the same great quality service.

Check Your Appointment Inventory

If you are like most people, you know that you can likely get your hands on an Apple product when you are ready to. But what most people don't realize is just how well Apple has worked to fine-tune their supply operations. When the company shifted its current inventory model, it had a massive problem on its hands. It had over sixty days' worth of inventory sitting in its supply chain. Today, they have brought that number down to a mere seven days. That's right, if Apple stops making iPhones and iPads in China today, within seven days there wouldn't be a single product for sale on any shelf in any country on the planet. Think about that amazing fact for just a minute.

Apple has fine-tuned its capacity issue so well that consumers have come to expect that they *can* get an Apple product, but they may occasionally have to wait in line for one, or order it online, or wait until the following week. Apple would never, however, make customers wait a month for an order to come in, and neither should you make your patients wait a month. If new patients—or any patients—are getting their braces off and want a certain day and time in your schedule, then your job is to do what you can to make that date and time possible.

Think of appointment inventory, capacity, and appearing too busy or unavailable in a different light. Think of it in terms of the high school prom for a moment. When I was growing up, if you didn't have a plan of action as prom was approaching, you would end up being left out in the cold without a prom date. Coming from a small town where we spent as much time focused on football as we did on the shine and wax of our classic muscle cars, being alone on prom night was about as popular as a worm in a punch bowl. If there is someone you had your eye on to take to the prom, the last thing you would want to do is appear as though you are unavailable for years, or that you are dating or hanging out with the same girl all the time. If you did that, everyone would assume you would be going to the prom with *her*. In other words, they would assume you were already busy—just as people do with your current practice.

There is a lot that goes into setting the tone for the image that you want to portray. It's very likely you are putting forth an image of a very busy doctor who is bustling from one task to the next. Whether that is really what your office is like, or it's just how the patient sees it, this image is something that you will need to give serious consideration.

The impression you put forth is important, especially when it comes to whether or not someone is going to refer your office. The good news is that you control that image and can take strides toward letting your patients see another side of your practice. You hold the cards that determine how your patients see you, so you want to make sure you play your hand in a way that will bring you more referrals.

CHAPTER TWO

REASON #2: INADEQUATE KNOW-HOW— THEY DON'T REFER BECAUSE THEY DON'T KNOW HOW OR DON'T HAVE ADEQUATE TOOLS.

NOW THAT WE'VE DISCUSSED THE TOP REASON WHY PEOPLE ARE NOT REFERRING YOU— they think you're busy enough already—we can move on to the next most important reason people don't refer. I've seen this through personal experience and from working with many other practices: people don't refer because they don't know how or don't have the proper tools.

A vital component in building a successful referral system is determining exactly *what* you should have in it and *how* the system should work. You can ask anyone to tell their friends about you, but that isn't going to help you have a consistent message. Nor is that going to give you control over *what* is communicated about your office, services, or the way you work.

Having a referral system that has been created with care will ensure that you have addressed these issues and will get the most out of your referrals. In other words, your word-of-mouth will not be done haphazardly. Rather, you will know *who* is referring, *what* they are referring, and even at times *when* the referring is being done.

GIVE THEM THE *PROPER* TOOLS

One of the biggest problems I find is that people don't know *how* to refer someone to others. If it's not something they are used to doing, they may not even know how, so they leave it alone and do nothing at all. Sure, they could just blurt out that so-and-so is a great doctor. But is that really an effective or meaningful referral? No, it's not. The person on the receiving end of that message may not even be in the market for a doctor, so the message will simply fall on deaf ears.

Furthermore, your patient—or even dentists in your area—may not know the right things to say that will actually motivate the person listening to pick up the phone and make an appointment with your office. There's a big difference in someone merely talking about your office and someone being able to prompt the person listening to make a call and become a patient.

Many people are unsure how to start a conversation that involves referring someone. They don't want to come off like they are giving a sales pitch or seem pushy. Or they may not even think about referring your office even though you meet their expectations when they visit. They may be satisfied, but making a referral just isn't something that crosses their mind unless someone *specifically* asks them if there is a doctor they can recommend.

When people have the proper tools—they know how to go about referring your office— you are more likely to get those referrals. The easier you make it for someone to refer you, the better off you will be. To be honest, most people tend to be on the lazy side when it comes to giving out referrals. It's not that they mean to be, but it's just the nature of referrals. So when we make things easy, people tend to refer more. And as an entrepreneur who wants referrals, it's your job to help make it easy for them.

> One of the biggest problems I find is that people don't know **how** to refer someone to others.

Most doctors I have worked with have no tools in place to help their patients make a good quality referral to their practice. Without putting in the effort to create any referral tools, doctors typically assume that their patients will know the right things to say to make referrals. Yet that is not reality.

But even if you've never thought much about a referral system, you can implement what you learn in these pages to quickly begin seeing the benefits of having an effective referral system in place.

MAKE GIVING REFERRALS EASY

To get more referrals, you have to make it easy for people to send them to you. There are some simple ways you can do this, especially in today's world of online networking and social media.

Online Sharing Options

You can post helpful information, and then prompt them to share it with someone by adding a button or tool that invites them to "share with a friend." You can do this on your website or with your company newsletter. Social media tools also offer you an easy way to help people refer your office. For example, you can post things on your Facebook page and ask them to tag a friend or share it with others, and within seconds, people can recommend you to their family and friends. Simple tools like that help make it easy for them to refer your office and share your information. When they share your information, post, or newsletter, they are automatically placing their stamp of approval on your practice.

But you can also use the platform to be social with your patients. You can do this with a variety of platforms—including a blog, Facebook, Twitter, etc. By interacting with them, you are giving them a chance to interact with you in a non-office atmosphere; and people like when your office takes the time to interact, answer questions, and provide helpful information. This, in turn, makes them even more willing to refer you.

Printed Materials

You can get creative with the various ways you provide tools to your patients and referring dentists, but consider things like printing helpful reports and pertinent articles for your office. Be sure to write something like "share this with a friend," to prompt them to do so. You can then offer the materials to those who may want to pass them on to a friend.

ENCOURAGE REFERRALS BY FOCUSING ON THE PATIENT

In order to get referrals, it is important to turn the focus onto your patients. In doing so, you will pay more attention to making sure their experience in your office is anything but boring. You want to become an interesting part of their day, help put a smile on their face, and become someone they know well and trust. People only feel comfortable referring someone they trust and respect, so you want to be that type of person to every patient.

The patients who leave your office happy and feeling good are the ones who are going to talk about you. If their appointment is just another boring part of their day or something they check off their to-do list, then there is not going to be much to talk about. Give your patients something to talk about and most will end up doing just that with their friends, family, and even with strangers.

UNDERSTAND WHEN PEOPLE REFER

When people do talk about you, there are several reasons they may do so at a particular time. These are beyond your control, but it's good to know what they may be. People will refer you when they really want to help someone who is in need of a good resource, when they want to look smart (like they are in the "know"), and when they want to feel like they are a part of something. No matter where someone is talking and for whatever reason, you want it to be your office that they are referring, not your competitors'.

THERE IS SUCH A THING AS A BAD REFERRAL

In some situations, not only do the patients lack the skills that are necessary to make a good referral, but they also end up using the wrong skills and make a bad referral, or they end up discouraging other referrals. They do this without even realizing that is what is happening.

You may be wondering what I mean by a bad referral, but once I share this story, you will know exactly what I mean.

An endodontist's patient telling a story about visiting the office for service may not necessarily be a bad thing. But when that patient sits around with a few close friends and tells them over lunch about her recent root canal experience, it works to the endodontist's disadvantage. By describing the experience in detail, she is actually discouraging and frightening her friends, who in turn are actually being pushed away from ever calling that office for an appointment. Without even realizing it, she is pairing a negative or uncomfortable experience with that endodontist; and she ends up making a negative impact.

This happens even though she likes the office and doctor. She is just sharing her experience with the procedure itself, but her friends tune in to the worrisome parts and overlook the fact that she is actually happy with the endodontist. All they hear are the details of a procedure they don't want anything to do with. Add to that all the other root canal stories they have heard from others, and now that practice is perpetually associated with those stories and fears. You can bet that endodontist will never get a new patient from among those listening at that table.

POWERFUL TOOLS FOR YOUR REFERRAL SYSTEM

Special Reports

For years, both in my practices and in the practices of my coaching clients, I have successfully used a special report of the month so that patients have a specific tool to share with a friend or family member. For example, if I want to reach more patients who need traditional metal braces, or perhaps mothers who have questions about their child's thumb-sucking habit, I can effectively reach these populations by creating a special report to answer some of their common questions. I discuss the problem, provide some solutions for the patient, and encourage them to call my office. This report is then inserted in the monthly newsletter, placed in high-traffic areas of the office, mailed directly to segments of our list, and distributed to referring dentists and medical colleagues, as well as being advertised and available online.

What I have found is that existing patients may take the special report to help their friend or neighbor solve a problem. Meanwhile, because we have created this report, we can take comfort that the message is consistent with what we know gets patients to call and schedule with our office. By creating something professional and helpful, the patient feels relaxed about calling us, rather than fearful like when hearing about a friend's root canal procedure.

*We don't **expect** patients to talk about us, and we certainly don't leave the conversation up to chance.*

Published Books

Another powerful referral tool we have used over the years is published books. With our published books, we delve into a specific topic of interest, providing more information than we would in one of our shorter special reports. The additional information helps the potential patients by offering solutions for them, which will then lead them to our office. The books allow us gain their trust and are successful in encouraging them to call our office for an appointment.

We don't *expect* patients to talk about us, and we certainly don't leave the conversation up to chance. We provide each patient with two copies of one of our books, along with clear instructions to share one with a friend or family member. We say, "Asking for referrals can be difficult, so when you're talking over the backyard fence with your friends and neighbors and the topic turns to braces, just hand them a copy of our book and say 'these are the people we know and trust.'" In addition to providing a wealth of information, published books allow you to be consistent in your message and establish you as an authority on the topic.

Audio and Video

Something else I use successfully in my practice to earn referrals are audio and video tools. Each day on YouTube, there are billions of videos viewed, adding up to hundreds of millions of hours. People love to watch videos and listen to audio recordings. Both are excellent tools for educating your patients on how to refer to your practice. Putting in the effort to create a series of helpful videos that are online and easy to access will provide you with one more way to reach people.

One thing that makes videos great, besides that fact that so many people like to watch them, is that they are available when the people need them. Whether your video library is accessible on your website, on YouTube, or through links on social media, when someone needs information on that topic, the videos are there waiting for them. Keep them readily available and offer them periodically to your followers on social media. If, for example, they know someone who may be dealing with a particular topic and they happen to see the video you post, they will end up sharing it with them.

Radio and TV

Radio interviews and special TV segments or interviews are powerful tools to establish you as an authority and for your office to gain influence in your area. When you assume your patients are aware of your interviews and news articles, you're light years away from where they are in their mind and where you are in your mind about your practice and the need for referrals. You must control every aspect you can, including the message, by providing tools for existing patients to refer their friends and family.

Reward Programs

Many businesses have reward programs in place to incentivize people to refer friends and family members. Consider Spin Pizza in Kansas City. It's a restaurant that you can't eat at without being asked to sign up for their rewards program. You can earn "Spin Bucks" toward future meals, free glasses of wine, gelato, and other goodies. Each time you visit, there's a new round of featured wines and beers. The menu changes seasonally so they can use the freshest locally-sourced ingredients.

The rewards club at Spin Pizza asks for your birthday, anniversary, and other pertinent details, such as if you are interested in catering deals, holiday party opportunities, etc. Spin Pizza encourages sharing the rewards program with friends and family and have prominent, yet classy, signage throughout the restaurant, along with take-home brochures, and emails with gifts on referral. This place also has a community newsletter with biking and cycling events as they have a big following of cycling fans, hence the name "Spin." It's no surprise they have grown from one location in Kansas City to nearly a dozen with expansion into Texas, Nebraska, and California.

They don't just hope you will talk about Spin Pizza with a friend, they make it easy and give you the tools to do so. When you make it easy for people to refer you by offering them tools and giving them excellent service, you have a winning combination on your hands. An excellent referral system and above-and-beyond service are the keys to having a practice that will grow to the level you want.

Effective Newsletters

Many practices send out newsletters, which is fine. But make sure you are sending out newsletters that contain *useful* information. According to research, only around a third of the people you send newsletters to are even going to open them. Even fewer will actually act on anything they learn from it. To get a higher read rate, be sure to focus on sending out quality content and have a catchy headline to entice them to open the newsletter. Inside the newsletter, add a button or link that makes it simple for the reader to "forward to a friend." Just having that small prompt will provide what the reader needs to refer you to another person.

One thing to keep in mind when sending out newsletters is that if you are just promoting your business, you are not doing it effectively. People will come to expect that if they open your newsletter, it will merely be a pitch for your office. So if they are not in need of services at the moment, they probably won't even click through to your newsletter. But if you provide them with quality content, more people will end up opening it; and they may even find something of value they will pass on to others. If they receive valuable information from your newsletter that helps solve a problem, your business will remain on their radar when they *do* need your services.

> *Many practices send out newsletters, which is fine. But make sure you are sending out newsletters that contain* **useful** *information.*

23

Your newsletter can be either electronic, or it can be in paper form. Whichever way you decide to go, be sure to have the suggestion on there that they pass it on to someone they know could use the information. Subtle messages like that can go a long way toward helping you to get more out of your referral tools.

Social Media

Many people who need services today begin their search online, often using social media. It's estimated that around 85 percent of people use the Internet to find local businesses. This makes it essential for your practice be online, and not only be there, but offer valuable information that will encourage web visitors to pick up the phone and make an appointment.

One of the most popular ways that people are finding out about businesses online is through social media. Social media includes blogs, Facebook, Twitter, YouTube, and a variety of other sites and services. The whole idea behind using social media is that it gives your office the opportunity to interact with your current and potential patients. Social media can be an effective tool when it comes to referrals. In fact, social media outlets are a popular way that various types of referrals are made today.

Being able to keep your message consistent is important, which means you should have someone managing your social media pages. Being able to post information and answer questions will go a long way toward getting your name out there. For example, if someone posts a question on your Facebook wall asking about a procedure, you should be ready to provide carefully selected information.

Every idea that comes to your mind is worth writing down and exploring.

And if one of your current patients posts good feedback on social media, you can thank them and post a link in case they have friends and family who would also be interested in learning more about whatever type of treatment they are receiving.

When someone posts on your wall or comments on your posts, their post or comment often shows up in their newsfeed, so their friends can see it, too. This offers an endorsement of sorts for those who see this interaction. It's a referral that is more subtle, yet effective. Not all social media sites are created equal and not all are going to be a good fit for your practice. But it's still import to leverage the benefits of social media for your business.

HOW TO DETERMINE YOUR REFERRAL TOOLS

There are a variety of tools that you can have at your disposal in order to help your patients refer your office. Consider, if you will, which five resources you could create or add that would enable your patients to refer your practice? Whether you use the ones that I have already mentioned or you come up with additional ones, start out with a list you can refer back to so you won't forget those great ideas.

Every idea that comes to your mind is worth writing down and exploring. You can brainstorm a list of ideas and then narrow it down to the top five that you think would be the best for you to start with. (Of course, you can always change your list later.) Once you have the ideas down on paper, you can begin to work on getting those resources into place one at a time.

WHAT *NOT* TO DO TO GET REFERRALS

In this book, you will learn a lot of good ways to get your patients to refer you. But it's important also to touch on a few of the bad ways, things you want to avoid doing.

Bogus or Paid Reviews

Many people use online review sites, writing their reviews and posting about their experiences with every type of business. But in today's world, there are so many fake referrals and fake reviews that it may be difficult for people to discern what's real and what's not. There are some businesses, believe it or not, that will even bribe or pay people to leave positive reviews.

As tempting as you may think it is, don't do anything that will come across as bribing people to give out your name as a referral. This means that you don't pay for reviews, you don't offer any type of monetary incentives or prizes, and you don't offer any favors in exchange for reviews or referrals.

The moment you offer some sort of bribe or accept fake reviews and referrals, you have just lost the trust of the consumer and damaged your business. People will wonder why you feel you need to do this in order to get someone to say something good about your practice.

Always avoid anything that will come across as looking like you paid for referrals or reviews. You want to *earn* those reviews and referrals, not twist arms and offer bribes to get them.

Stick to getting only the reviews that you honestly earn. Obtaining false or bribed reviews is a quick way to diminish your reputation if people find out, and readers can usually tell if a review is sincere or has been fabricated. Avoid doing anything that would be seen as immoral or dishonest when it comes to obtaining online reviews. Steer clear of that so you can maintain your reputation for the long haul and so that you know the people referring your office actually believe what they are saying.

This also goes for any published books you may have. It's okay to post a social media message that reminds people to leave a positive review if they liked your book, but it's a whole different one to pay or bribe people to write bogus reviews in order to make it look better. People are becoming increasingly aware of this dishonest practice, and even places like Amazon are looking for ways to crack down on it.

Paid "Likes" and Followers

Other ways that people are dishonest on social media is by purchasing "likes" from certain companies at a cheap price. For five bucks, you can get 1,000 new likes to your site. But this is not an honest approach to getting more people to follow you, and it can actually backfire. While you may gain a lot of likes overnight, they will not be quality ones, so they will not be engaged or give you any referrals. In fact, most of them come from bogus accounts that Facebook has been trying to weed out to avoid these exact issues. The last thing you want is to make it look like you have a lot of followers, and yet nobody engages in your posts. Ultimately, you get no referrals or response because they were not quality followers to begin with.

When you obtain reviews, likes, and followers through dishonest measures, you will never get referrals from them. So those efforts will be wasted. Focus your efforts only on getting honest referrals so that your integrity can never be questioned and you will get new patients for your efforts.

HOW TO DEAL WITH NEGATIVE REVIEWS

While we are on the topic, it's important to address negative reviews. Everything we have discussed thus far is about positive word-of-mouth, because that is what you want to focus on. But what happens if you log on one day to your social media or an online review site and you see that someone has left negative feedback about your services? What is the best way to handle that? While there is no surefire way to address it, there are some ways that are better than others.

Don't Ignore It

The most important thing to do is to *not* ignore any negative feedback. If you do, the bad review will stand on its own and will be what people see and believe. It will have a negative impact and may actually do the opposite of referring; it may turn away who potential patients.

Respond Professionally

Your best response is to reply to the review in a professional manner. Write that you apologize they had such an experience in your office, because that is not the quality standard that you set. Invite them to come back to your office so you can make things right and correct any issues. Thank them for bringing any shortcomings to your attention (even if you don't feel they have a legitimate problem to begin with).

When you respond to negative reviews this way, you take the wind out of their sails. They may have written something negative, but it was followed up with your professional handling of the issue. That shows others that you are responsive and care enough about your patients that you want to correct any issues. It may actually nullify the review's detrimental effect it could have had on potential referrals. It may even encourage those potential patients to choose your practice simply because they appreciate your honesty and the time you took to address the reviewer's concerns.

When it comes down to it, most people who have complaints are just looking for someone in your office to listen to them. If they feel nobody is listening, then they feel slighted. If they have a complaint and someone listens and tries to help them, then they are usually okay with things. You can save the relationship that way, and you can still gain new referrals from the review.

There is always a way to address negative online reviews, so you or someone in your office should be in charge of responding. When you do that, you not only temper the negativity, but you are controlling your message and image. It usually takes only seconds to respond, but it can have a big impact.

Deal with Slanderous Reviews

If you see a particular review that is slanderous in nature—and you *know* it is not true—try contacting the review site to let them know. Ask them to remove the slanderous information about your practice.

INTERACT WITH YOUR PATIENTS ON A DEEPER LEVEL

One of the best ways to get referrals from your patients and dentists is to have conversations. Rather than keeping everything strictly business and always being matter-of-fact, start a conversation that is not about treatment. If you know one of your patients loves soccer, bring up some games and ask if they play. If you know that patient has a birthday or an appointment coming up, see if you can surprise the person with a couple of tickets to the local game. Whatever it is, there are ways to have conversations with the person and to also surprise them, creating memories and building bonds with your office.

While you don't want to seem like a stalker, do make an effort to get to know your patients. Learn more about them, their interests, and the things that they like to do. Then find ways to start conversations about those things. When you show an interest in who they are as a person, rather than just as a patient you are treating, you will form meaningful connections. Those who feel connected will love your office. They'll want to come back again, and they'll be excited to tell others about your office. You will be providing them an experience that is above and beyond, rather than just meeting their expectations. Plus, when you can chat about something they love for even a minute, you will be anything but boring.

DON'T BE BORING

I've said this many times, and I'll say it many more—people don't talk about what is boring. If their visit to your office is the same old thing, then it won't stand out in their mind, and it's not going to get talked about much afterward. People don't share information about boring because nobody wants to listen to it. For the most part, boring simply isn't discussed.

So make every effort to ensure your office is interesting. If what you are doing is boring, you are not going to get referrals no matter what you do. This is especially an important thing to remember when it comes to spending your hard-earned dollars on advertising and marketing. While you may be pouring money into these things, they may be falling on deaf ears if what you are putting out there isn't interesting.

When you put out ads, promotional materials, or whatever it is that you are doing, don't spend the money without first asking if what you are doing is boring. If it is, you have to change it before purchasing it or it will never give you the return on investment to make it worth your while. If what you are putting out there is interesting, fun, and memorable, then go for it. But still always track it to see if it is worth the effort or if further changes need to be made.

CHAPTER THREE

REASON #3: LACKLUSTER SERVICE— THEY DON'T REFER BECAUSE THEIR EXPERIENCE WITH YOUR PRACTICE IS ADEQUATE OR SUFFICIENT, BUT NOT EXTRAORDINARY.

IF YOU HAVEN'T DONE MUCH TO ENSURE YOU HAVE AN ADEQUATE REFERRAL SYSTEM IN PLACE, then you probably haven't gone out of your way to wow your current patients either. Most people don't fully see the connection between the two without it being brought to their attention. But the connection is not only there, it is crucial in order to get more referrals from your current patients and from the dentists in your area.

When you stop and think about this connection, though, it makes a lot more sense.

PEOPLE DON'T REFER "OKAY" SERVICE

Have you ever dined at a restaurant and thought that the food was okay? You were satisfied, but it wasn't great? How many people are you interested in telling about this place that was just okay? You are likely not in much of a hurry to tell anyone at all. And why would you be? Who walks around bragging about a place that is just okay? There are okay places all around, so it's nothing special to talk about with others, unless someone is looking for just an okay place to go to. And how many people are doing that?

It's hard to consider this idea as a possibility, but it may be a reason that people are not referring your office. Are you giving them great service that makes them want to talk about it with others?

Be honest with yourself for just a few minutes. It's a tough question, but if the answer is no—or that you could absolutely be doing better—then you may have found a major part of the problem of why you are not getting referrals. You have to really look at the service you and your entire office are providing and then ask if this is a possibility.

A mother once told me that she shared on a social media site that she found a dentist she really liked. She thought he was awesome. But every time she went for an appointment, the receptionist was rude to her. She felt the receptionist would treat her like she was a bother and was downright rude to her on a regular basis. The patient was at a point where she was torn between continuing to go see a dentist she was really happy with and putting up with the mistreatment from the front office staff.

I asked the woman if she had ever mentioned to the dentist about how unhappy she was with the office treatment, and she said no. Not only did she not want to upset him or get people in trouble, speaking up about it was something she was uncomfortable doing.

Even if you are making sure you provide excellent service to your patients, that doesn't mean everyone in your office is. When you evaluate whether your practice is providing extraordinary service, you have to look at everyone in the office. How many times do you think this woman would want to refer that practice to her friends and family? Most likely never, because although she liked the dentist, she didn't want her friends to be treated poorly by the receptionist either. So not only will this dentist lose one patient if he doesn't find out about the deficit in the front office, it's likely costing him referrals, too.

Everyone on your team has to be on board with providing excellent service, no matter what position they are in. Not everyone knows how to do this right off, so be sure to give them the proper training they need to offer great customer service so they can provide it on behalf of your practice. Great resources exist for you and your team to get the training you need. The Ritz-Carlton Leadership Training Center and The Disney Institute, along with Burleson Seminars live training events, all provide practice, step-by-step service improvement programs that can take your team to the next level. Give people *extraordinary* service and they will be more apt to refer their family and friends.

HOW TO OFFER EXTRAORDINARY SERVICE

In all likelihood, your patients' experience with your practice is adequate—and even sufficient—but it's not extraordinary. And you should want to be extraordinary. That's where you start reaching goals and setting new records. If you can't say that your practice referral system is extraordinary, then make changes now to get it to that level. It will take effort on your part to get it started, but once you have the system in place, it can pretty much run on autopilot.

You have probably never thought about this, but the truth is that nobody leaves your office and runs home, short of breath, bursting through the door to proudly and wildly proclaim "Honey, come quick! You're not going to believe what the orthodontist is doing."

If you have been assuming that providing great customer service was enough to get you referrals, stop thinking that way. In today's consumer- and buyer-centric economy and market, your patients already assume they are going to get great service. Getting great service comes with the territory, and they pretty much expect that is going to be the minimum of what they get at your office. Providing great service just means you met their minimum expectations. Nobody refers an orthodontist or dentist who simply meets their expectations. They only refer ones who *exceed* them.

Quite honestly, if all you are doing is providing your patients with good service, then you deserve a paycheck, not a referral. To get a referral, you will have to go *way* above and beyond what your patients expect. You will have to surprise them, wow them, and excite them. Trust me, you can do that; and you will be amazed at how quickly you begin getting quality referrals when you do.

> Everyone on your team has to be on board with providing excellent service, no matter what position they are in.

Think about places like Disney and Nordstrom for a moment. They make a habit of sharing stories of exceptional customer service when one of their employees or cast members has gone *way* above and beyond to create a memorable experience for their guests. They only share the ones that they know are going to get the guests or customers talking when they get home. They never share stories about just meeting customer's or guest's expectations, and neither do your patients. They are only going to go home talking about their experience and referring you to others if you have far exceeded their expectations. So your goal is to give them something that will be worth sharing with others when they leave your office.

In fact, a news station or paper wouldn't even pick up the story and share it with their readers unless the service or experience provided had gone way above and beyond. Doing something extraordinary makes people talk, and it gets others interested. People can get their expectations met all day long at just about any place in town. But they can't go just anywhere to be wowed or have their expectations greatly exceeded.

It's time to think of those things you can do to impress your patients. Disney, for example, will provide your child with a special certificate if they are not tall enough for a certain ride. Rather than being disappointed, they walk away happy because the certificate entitles the child to be first in line for the ride next year when they will be tall enough to ride it. Their cast members are always on the lookout to make guest visits far exceed expectations, and as a result Disney has no shortage of people who rave about what an incredible time they and their children had during their visit. It's a small gesture on their part, but it carries with it a lot of weight.

Once, after a young child reached the front of a line with her ice cream cone still unfinished, a Disney cast member overheard the little girl ask her mother, "But who is going to hold my ice cream when I'm on the ride?" The cast member didn't hesitate to step in and help with the family's experience by saying, "Hi there! I will hold your ice cream and it will be here when you get back." Without asking for a supervisor's permission, the employee walked over to the nearest ice cream stand and purchased a new ice cream cone a few minutes before the time she knew the young guest would return. The little girl never knew the difference, but the lasting impression on the mother has resulted in return trips for years and countless referrals to Disney. The stories of how Disney goes above and beyond for their customers is endless, which is why they remain such a successful business.

HOW TO WOW YOUR PATIENTS

How are you giving your patients something to talk about? What are you doing to "wow" them? If you don't know the answer to those questions, you are probably not doing much. This gives patients very little to talk about with others and very little reason to refer your office. The more you learn about what some other places are doing to surprise and impress their customers, the easier it is to see the connection between their actions and why we all know those businesses so well.

The good thing about wowing your patients is that it doesn't have to be expensive.

Nordstrom is known for wowing their customers. They have the best no-hassle return policy I've ever seen. They are famous for the customer service they provide when a person returns something. If you buy a pair of shoes that you are not happy with, they will take them back, even years later and even if they no longer carry that specific shoe. A customer even brought back tires that she said were purchased at Nordstrom. The associate, fully aware that Nordstrom does not sell tires, could have flatly refused and turned her away. Instead, he issued a full refund for what the customer claimed she had paid for the tires. How he went about handling such a return claim says a lot about the type of business they are and the customer service they provide.

How do you deal with refund requests at your practice? Are full refunds issued promptly and courteously when patients are dissatisfied with your office? Or are you like most businesses, where returning a product or getting a refund requires answering more questions than returning to a politically unstable country on a temporary visa?

Your goal should be to model Nordstrom when it comes to providing people with refunds. This will impress your patients and they will share that information with others. People will see that providing excellent customer service, no questions asked, is the norm at your business. Knowing that if they are unhappy they can get a refund—without a ton of questions and hurdles to jump over—will go a long way toward helping patients feel comfortable going to your office. It has even resulted in referrals for our office. Once a patient posted in a review she changed from a one star to a five star with this testimonial, "Yes, I had a difficult experience but they went above and beyond to help me and I can see why people like it here so much."

INEXPENSIVE WAYS TO WOW YOUR PATIENTS

The good thing about wowing your patients is that it doesn't have to be expensive. You don't have to start accounting for a big budget to try and get their attention and go above and beyond. It's often the little things that are overlooked—like the Disney cast member holding an ice cream cone—that impress people and go a long way toward wowing them. Look for low-cost and no-cost ways to wow your patients every day.

There are many ways you can do this: remembering them by their name and then referring to them on a first-name basis, taking "social notes" on what your patients are up to (e.g., the sports or instruments they are playing, hobbies they enjoy, classes that are exciting to them right now in school, etc.), being on time when they come in for their appointment, and personally greeting them in a way that shows you remember them (e.g., remember their profession or the part of town they live in). You can ask, "How is our favorite 6th grade teacher today? Are those kids driving you crazy yet?" or "What's the traffic like down in Brookside? Did they finally get your street finished with all that construction?"

Other ideas that won't cost you a lot of money include sending little birthday notes or TLC cards when the patient has something big and exciting going on in their life. Or you can keep billing records on file for easy retrieval and give patients the ability to charge a card on file securely through encryption with a simple approval by the parent. Assure your patients with this question: "We can email you the receipt or print it for you. Which would you prefer?"

It's easy to wow your patients if you are paying attention to them. When you do that, you will pick up on small things about them, such as the sports teams they love, the hobbies they are passionate about, or what their favorite food may be. By remembering some of those things, you will make a connection that helps them feel that you care more about them than being just another patient getting treatment. The fact that you care enough to ask them about things that they are interested or involved in will be sure to wow them. And that doesn't cost a dime. It only requires that you pay attention.

You don't even have to try to remember all of these things about your patients. It's a great idea to keep a little note in their file that lists a few of these things so you can refer to it upon meeting with them. After a while you will begin to remember them, and the reference note will no longer be necessary.

On the flip side, the last thing your patient wants is to tell about something they love or do for a living only to have you completely forget it when it's brought up again a month later.

Another good way to connect with your patients and wow them is to find common ground. Look for something that you both like, even if it's a sports team, movie, or type of dessert. You can do this, but so can others on your team. The more common ground you can find between your patient and your office, the better.

These are just some of the simple, low-cost and no-cost ways you can "wow" your patients. They are small touches that far too many service businesses have forgotten, yet they mean a lot to the patient.

DO SWEAT THE SMALL STUFF

What many doctors I work with don't realize is that it is usually the small things that matter the most to patients. We tend to overlook them because they are small and therefore we feel that must mean they are insignificant.

But the truth is that many of the things that win customers over and result in massive referrals to your office are simple. That isn't to say that they are easy; far too many businesses fail to consistently perform them. Yet they are things that are incredibly simple.

Some of those little, simple things that win customers over include saying what you are going to do and then following through with it, showing up on time, and saying please and thank you. These are all simple strategies that my mother taught me before kindergarten; but how many of your friends, family, and business colleagues fail to do what they said they would do? How many show up late to a meeting or dinner? How many fail to send a simple thank-you note after a gift has been received? And how many have stopped asking, "Can you please help me with this?"

People are craving good old exceptional service when they do business.

Believe it or not, this comes down mostly to minding common manners. In fact, I find that good manners make up more than 50 percent of providing exceptional service. If you don't believe this simple truth, go take a commercial airline flight or visit your doctor and see how long you wait, how insincerely you are greeted, and how you are treated. Pay attention to whether or not they thank you for your business.

There used to be a time when you got a lollipop and a handshake, or a pat on the head, at the doctor's office, along with a seat big enough to relax in and real food on every airline flight. Today, companies and service industry leaders providing anything near this level of experience are dominating their competition.

People are craving good old exceptional service when they do business. Word-of-mouth is a huge source of business for the places that get this right, because they are offering something that others are overlooking or simply not seeing the value in.

Take a moment to compare your favorite restaurant to the latest trend in mid-level service providers, such as places like Chili's, Applebee's, and the Delta airline terminals. These businesses are equipped with iPads and WiFi, giving you the ability to order food and beverages right from your seat without any interaction with a server. Although the practice has certainly reduced the variable cost of labor through technology—and likely reduced employee theft of cash and recording of customer credit card numbers (a significant source of identity theft and fraudulent credit card charges each year)—these restaurants are dropping the ball on two significant issues.

The first is that no one comes by to check on me, the customer; and the little iPad doesn't prompt me to order another glass of wine or have some dessert. I have to go through the ordering process again if I want something like that. Sales certainly have to be lower without a live person asking me if I want a refill or some dessert. More importantly, however, is that I'm not referring my friends and family to go see an iPad. Why would I? There's no interaction or connection being made there at all. That level of customer service basically tells me they don't want to be bothered with me, so they give me an iPad to avoid having to actually provide me with one-on-one customer service.

On the flip side, however, I absolutely do frequently refer my friends and family to my favorite restaurants and tell them specifically to "Ask for Paul or Sandy, my favorite waiter or waitress. Tell them Dustin sent you." I'm making the referral for the exceptional service as much as I am for the food. Give me *good* food and a great human server versus exceptionally *great* food and an iPad, and I'll refer people to the human server every single time.

Good customer service has become something that is hard to find in today's digital world. People are often being replaced by computers, recorded messages, and machines of all sorts that will do the job of the person who used to do it. The problem with this, as I've pointed out, is that you cannot bond and interact with a computer device. You will never get to know the computer or feel cared about by it, and you won't ever feel compelled to tell others to go see the computer at a particular place because it will treat you right.

If your practice focuses on the little things and can provide exceptional customer service in this world that is often lacking it, you will be far ahead of the competition, and you will receive many referrals because of it.

GO THE EXTRA MILE

If you think about the number of businesses you interact with on a weekly or monthly basis, you can see that it's quite a few. In fact, it's a lot. We get into a habit of going about our routine, interacting with these businesses all week long, often to the point that it becomes second nature. We pull into a gas station and fuel up, but we are so dazed we don't even realize what we did. As we drive away from the pump, it may finally register that we just filled up our tank.

But that would never have happened thirty years ago, because you used to get personal customer service when you pulled up to the fuel pump. Someone would ask you what gas you would like and how much, and they would clean your windows and maybe even check your oil.

Today, because of the lack of customer service that goes the extra mile, we often go through the motions as if we are perpetually on autopilot. Very little interaction happens between the customer and the business providing the services or products. Those businesses that go the extra mile to provide excellent customer service—especially covering the little things—will stand out and be remembered.

For example, take luxury car dealerships like Lexus and BMW. When customers take their cars into these dealerships for service, the employees go above and beyond to care for your vehicle. They wash the mats, vacuum the interior, and even wash the car before returning it to the owner. How many service stations have you been to that have left grease stains on your door handle or floor mats? What are the odds that you will refer someone to that business? What if the business just performs to your expectations, providing you with work that is timely, on or under budget, and without any additional work or hassle on your part, such as having to ask them to clean off the stain they left on your car?

Consider the type of business you would want to refer to your friends and family. Ask yourself what it is about those particular businesses that makes them worthy of your referral, and take note of those qualities. My guess is they will make your preferred referral list because they are going the extra mile and standing out. You don't go through their line or do business with them on autopilot. You are engaged, impressed, and have made a connection to the business.

Make it a goal to be that type of business.

OFFER A HIDDEN SECRET

Perhaps your office can offer a hidden secret in your customer service that turns out to be a gem and brings you plenty of referrals. Years ago, this worked with Cary Grant. He had an Italian tailor in Hollywood who would add a dazzling pocket square at no charge. He would then spritz the pocket square in his bespoke suits with a unique fragrance from Italy. Not only did Mr. Grant go on to refer many of his Hollywood friends and movie stars to his favorite tailor, but he also created a large following for the successful, if somewhat "hidden secret," which was the men's fragrance called Acqua di Parma.

In our practices, we share stories of exceptional customer service with new employees to show that we walk the walk, or what we call "crawling through broken glass for our customers…it only hurts for a little while." We share stories such as the parents who called at 10 p.m. with a broken appliance and were leaving for vacation out of the country the next morning on a Sunday, and the clinical assistant and doctor who came into the office at midnight to help them. We share stories of how we have had patients and parents with broken retainers or aligners, and the employees who have driven replacement appliances to their house, or even to a soccer game or restaurant, so that the family's schedule was not interrupted. We share the examples of families in financial hardship with parents who have lost their jobs and our ability to secure treatment for them through Smiles Change Lives or our own nonprofit foundation.

We want people to know those stories. Not because we are just out to brag, because we are not. We want to show patients that we are willing to provide the exceptional customer service they crave. Our office is willing to go the extra mile and to wow our patients. We care about their personal experience with our office; and if there are things we can do to help make it a better experience and to far exceed their expectations, we want to do it. That's what gets us a dedicated patient who is happy to share with others the experience they have received through our office.

> **!** *Consumers and patients still want exceptional service that goes the extra mile.*

We share all of these stories with others for another reason, too. They remind our existing employees of appropriate and expected behavior and set the bar for new employees in their quest to adapt to our culture.

Without stories like this, companies can quickly forget where they came from and what has driven their success up to this point. We like to call this "dance with the one who brought you." Our patients, community leaders, referring dentists, and vendors have all contributed massively to our success. We feel it is our moral duty and obligation to not only serve them, but to massively exceed their expectations. Without this level of "wow" service, we do not expect, nor should patients feel obligated to refer our practice to their friends and family.

You have to give your patients a reason to refer your office. If you don't go the extra mile to do this, then don't be surprised when they don't refer. To be honest, you just haven't earned their referral if all you have done is simply meet their expectations.

Be the office that makes people say "nobody does that." When you offer to go the extra mile, you will stand out and people will talk. People still want their gas pumped for them, their windows wiped, their oil changed. They want that, but nobody seems to be offering it anymore. My guess is that if a gas station charged a few more cents per gallon and offered it again, people would line up to get that kind of service. That's because nobody does it anymore.

Determine what it is that nobody does in your area, and then do it. By offering it, you will be motivating patients to talk about what you are doing because it's so rare. Yet it's so wanted and appreciated.

It's not that customers stopped wanting individualized human service when they dine out, or that they no longer wanted someone to pump their gas for them. It's not that consumers want self-checkout lanes at the grocery store because they no longer want to speak with a cashier. These changes have nothing to do with demands and preferences from the customers. They have everything to do with the decisions that businesses have made on their own, or at the prompting of someone who has found ways for these companies to "save money." Although one has to wonder how much money they are saving, or missing out on, by not providing exceptional customer service. Not only have they likely lost some customers who don't appreciate the lack of genuine service, but they also lose out on many referrals. People are not going to refer places like that, so they are essentially leaving money on the table.

Consumers and patients still want exceptional service that goes the extra mile. At a time when it is getting increasingly more difficult for them to find it, the few companies who do offer it—and make it a priority—will thrive. They will be doing what nobody else does, and their reward is they will end up automatically getting many referrals for their actions.

Don't wait for your patients to demand great service or amazing features and tools. Be a step ahead of them in providing it to them. They want to talk, but you have to give them something to talk about.

APPLYING IT TO YOUR PRACTICE

Think about your own practice and the customer service experience that your office provides. Describe three areas of your patient experience that you can honestly identify as being adequate, but not exceptional. How can you improve them so that your service is over-the-moon outrageous and patients are can't help talking about you to their friends and family? What can you do to make your service to them so good that they simply feel they *have* to share that referral with others? Using this information, you can begin to see what areas of your customer service need an overhaul.

It is also important that your staff be on board with this. Those who work for you must know the mission of providing excellent service and the importance of wowing your patients. Give them the ability to provide some great service on the spot, without having to put the person on hold while they ask for permission. When people can just go the extra mile without having to get permission for it, the patient will see that everyone in the office feels it is important to provide exceptional customer service.

CUSTOMER SERVICE TRAINING

On this note, it is important to bring up proper training for those working in your office. Most job training doesn't include lessons on how to go the extra mile for patients; instead, people usually just learn the basics. But the basics are what will just meet the expectations of your patients. It won't take them past that, and it won't give patients something to talk about.

Knowing this, it is your job to ensure your staff is properly trained in the area of not just providing customer service, but in providing *exceptional* and *beyond-the-call-of-duty* customer service. Discuss it with them, demonstrate it, and let them know it is a priority in your office. Get them the proper training and tools they need in order to be great on your office's behalf. The resources mentioned earlier in the book, like Burleson Seminars, The Disney Institute and Ritz-Carlton Leadership Training Center, are all great places to start, but don't forget the importance of proper oversight and compliance with your service standards. Only by consistently secret-shopping your office locations every month will you discover if your customer service goals are being achieved. The Mystery Shopping Providers Association (MSPA) has plenty of resources available to help you develop a quality-assurance program, including the hiring and management of secret shoppers in your area. Visit www.MysteryShop.org for more information

When you begin to focus on providing your customers with the type of service that will make them want to talk, beautiful things happen. You will love making them that happy, and they will be talking about and referring your office. The referrals will naturally follow once you have established your practice as the one that does what nobody else does—goes above and beyond, and is providing exceptional service. Putting these things in place may take some effort, but it will be well worth it in the long run.

CHAPTER FOUR

REASON #4: ORDINARY WELCOME— THEY DON'T REFER BECAUSE THEY ARE NOT WELCOMED TO YOUR PRACTICE IN A BIG WAY.

I'VE LEARNED A LOT OVER THE YEARS ABOUT WHY IT IS THAT PEOPLE DON'T TAKE THE TIME OR put in the effort to refer. There are numerous reasons, as I've described already, but one of the big ones comes down to how new patients are welcomed at your office. While it may seem like this is not that big of a deal, if you dig a little deeper, you will see that it's actually a major issue. But the good news is that it's also one you have control over and can quickly turn around in your favor.

MAKE NEW PATIENTS FEEL REALLY WELCOME

What does your office do to welcome a new patient? If you are like most doctors in the field, not a whole lot. And that's not who you want to be. The patient usually shows up for a long-awaited appointment and slips into the waiting room without any fanfare, and then you say hello to them when you enter the room—nothing special, that's for sure. Nothing to make them feel really welcome at your office, like they are the one patient you have been waiting for—even though that's how *every* patient should be made to feel.

A new patient will remember when you make them feel welcome and that you are glad to have them at your office. They will appreciate it and will want to come back again, as well as tell others about it. There are many ways you can go about doing this, but don't be afraid to think big to really make an impression.

Considering sending them a gift, having a surprise at the office for them, or putting together a new patient welcome package? Maybe give them something like a gift certificate to a local photographer, where they can go to get pictures taken of their beautiful, new smile once treatment has been completed.

Whatever you do, do *something* to welcome your new patients to your office. That way you will stand out, and they will feel they made the right choice about going to your office.

DON'T IGNORE YOUR CURRENT PATIENTS

But while you are putting a lot of attention on the new patients, never forget your returning patients. They are the backbone of your business, and they should also be welcomed in a big way. Always go out of your way to not only welcome them to the office, but to make them feel special and appreciated. When you are having a conversation with them, ask them what their favorite beverage is. If, for example, they say they are a Starbucks fan, be sure to make a note of it. A few weeks later, surprise them by mailing a Starbucks gift card to them. Add a little note that says "Here are two drinks on us. Enjoy!" or something along those lines. It's a small expense to pick up, but will go a long way toward making them feel appreciated and getting them to refer you to their friends and family. If they get something like that in the mail, they will want to spread the word about how you go above and beyond to make your patients feel special.

HOW TO WELCOME BIG

Welcome your patients—new and returning—in a big way. When you do that, they will want to refer your practice in a big way, too. There are numerous ways you can do this, and you are not bound to following any specific rules. Get creative with it so you can really surprise your new patients. Give them something to talk about.

Remember, people don't talk about boring. But if you surprise them with your welcome, they will absolutely talk about it. They will *have* to talk about it, because it's so different to get such a big welcome as a new patient.

In addition to keeping gift cards on hand, which are always a popular and surprising way to welcome people, there are other things you can do. Some of them may cost money, but others do not. They simply go back to the good old-fashioned, excellent service that people are craving, but often not getting.

Here are some additional suggestions for how you can welcome your new patients in a big way:

- **Welcoming patients in a big way starts when the first phone call is received.** When someone calls to make their first appointment, they should be welcomed so they know your office *wants* to see them. This means their appointment shouldn't be put off for six to eight weeks as many doctors do. Would it make you feel welcome if you had to wait two months to get in for your first appointment? Probably not, and it doesn't appeal to your new patients either. Every effort should be made to get them in for their appointment in a timely manner.

- **Prior to your new patients coming into the office, send them a personal note saying you are looking forward to meeting them at their appointment.** You could also send them a new patient welcome kit that includes information and frequently asked questions. If you really want to surprise them, throw in a Starbucks gift card.

    Whatever you do, do **something** *to welcome your new patients to your office.*

- **When new patients arrive for their first appointment, they should be greeted in a personal way, including having someone welcome them to your office and refer to them by name.** Maybe show them around a little, making sure they know where the restrooms are, rather than sending them directly to the waiting room to figure things out on their own.

- **Put in some effort to make your patient waiting area welcoming.** Have some water available, as well as some reading material. This is a great place to have one of your own custom "new patient welcome" brochures.

- **As their new doctor, it is important that they get a genuine personal introduction from you.** Rather than walk into the room and get right down to business, take a minute to introduce yourself, welcome them to your office, and chat for a minute to help them feel comfortable and to make sure they know you appreciate their decision to come to your office.

- **One of the biggest complaints that patients have today is the lack of individual attention they feel they get from their doctors.** They want to be more than a number or the next one in line for treatment. When you see them as an individual who has made the conscious decision to choose your office over your competitor's, then you will want to give them a big welcome. By taking the time do so and by speaking to them one-on-one, as well as listening to them, you will create a great first impression. You will start laying the foundation for building a connection. Those connections are what keep people coming back and keep them referring your office.

CONSIDER YOUR OWN EXPERIENCES

If you think about the ways in which you have been welcomed to new places, you begin to understand how important the big welcome is. Think about the last time you were welcomed to a business in a really big way. It doesn't happen often, but places such as luxury hotels, high-end clothiers, furniture stores, home remodelers, car dealerships, and exceptionally-astute small businesses

> **!** *It's hard to stay grumpy when everyone is making a big deal about welcoming you to the practice.*

are usually adept at making you feel welcome. They go the extra mile to make you feel important, valued, and appreciated for coming in. They let you know they are grateful that you made the decision to do business with them.

How did it make you feel when the business acted like they truly appreciated your stopping in? Would you describe your feelings toward that business as more or less likely to refer a friend or family member? How did it make feel about any purchases you made there? Were you, like most people would be, excited, confident, and enthusiastic to return to the business for future purchases?

As a business owner, you have an important and crucial job when it comes to your patients. You have the ability to make them feel great about choosing to do business with you, making them feel indifferent about the decision, or making them feel remorseful and that they wish they had chosen your competitor. It's important to consider this when deciding how your office as a whole will welcome all new patients. The average consumer has up to 70,000 thoughts per day, but only a half-dozen or so changes in mood or feeling. How do you want your patients to *feel* and what will you do to make them feel great about the decision they made?

PREVENT REGRET

No one wants to experience buyer's remorse. No matter what it is you have made the decision to purchase, you don't want to end up regretting that purchase later. Welcoming customers to a business is one way to reduce this negative emotion and to make the sale stick. But this is way more than just avoiding the negative feelings of buyer's remorse. If all you can do is make people feel "just okay" about doing business with you, then all you can hope for are average results and a low word-of-mouth referral rate.

On the other hand, when you welcome new patients to your practice in a big way, it essentially makes them want to talk about you to their friends and family. Good things like that automatically get shared with others, whether it's on Facebook, during a conversation at lunch, or the next time one of their friends is looking for a new doctor.

Some people may come into your office already assuming they will not be happy there. Perhaps they fear going for treatment, they have had a bad day, or they just have the type of attitude that leads them to see the negative in everything. By welcoming them in a big way, you are going to do a lot to help turn that negativity around and get the relationship off to a great start.

It's hard to stay grumpy when everyone is making a big deal about welcoming you to the practice. Even if they had anticipated buyer's remorse before ever stepping into your office—simply because that is their personality—you can do a lot to help change that with the way you give them a big welcome from the start.

Most of the time, it is the small gestures that businesses make that stick with us and stand out the most. Many of you know I travel a great deal because I provide a variety of services to doctors around the world, ranging from mentoring to delivering keynote speeches. I no longer travel as much as I did years ago when I was building our practice and lecturing on the topics of clinical orthodontics, marketing, business management, and patient relationship management through software automation. However, I still travel enough that the Ritz Carlton and Four Seasons make special notes on my loyalty and are always sure to welcome me to their property in a big way. It might be a bottle of wine and a meat, cheese, and fruit tray waiting for me in the room, or maybe it's a collection of t-shirts and hats for the boys. Sometimes it's a necktie or a golf item, but there is always—*always*—a handwritten note addressed to Dr. Burleson, welcoming me for the first time or welcoming me back to the property. This is something they always get right.

It's not an extremely expensive gift that they give, nor is it extremely difficult for them to procure a few items from the gift shop or in-room dining so they can provide a special thank-you. But it's certainly enough that I'm talking about it with you in this book and will continue to talk about it with thousands of orthodontists on stage and through my monthly newsletter. They are smart to take a small gift and exchange it for my loyalty and referrals.

Where in your practice are you ignoring the opportunity to reward loyalty and referrals? There are numerous places that you are. By identifying them now, you can make lasting changes to benefit your practice.

Turning it around to ensure you are rewarding loyalty and referrals takes two things. First, you have to put in the time. But once you get it all set up and everyone in your office is on board, then it should be something that runs on autopilot. The second thing it takes is an investment—but it doesn't have to be a large one. Don't shy away from the areas that may cost you a little bit of money. The return on investment from those efforts will be well worth your time, energy, and money.

MY EXPERIENCE WITH A SUPERB WELCOME

One place that I love to go because of the amazing way they welcome my family is the Ritz Reserve at Dorado Beach in Puerto Rico. At the time of this writing, it is only one of two Ritz Reserve properties in the world. The cheapest rooms start at $1,500 per night, and they include two dedicated personal assistants to your pre-arrival, stay, and departure.

Before arriving, the concierge at the property verifies the names and ages of everyone staying on the property. He also arranges what foods you would like stocked in your suite and any activities you'll be enjoying while on vacation. This includes luxury itineraries, such as cruising around the island for a few days on a 72-foot motor yacht and the helicopter the boys and I take to get to the boat, so that we can avoid a two-hour car ride to the marina.

Expensive itineraries aside, even without such upgrades, the entire hotel staff is alerted to our arrival in the prearranged private transportation; and upon arrival, the boys are greeted by name. ("You must be Samuel, and this is William, right? And that makes you Benjamin, then, doesn't it?") As the boys are greeted, they are given homemade popsicles. Let me tell you, if you want to wow a new customer, try coordinating a popsicle delivery in the middle of the Caribbean heat and humidity. Those suckers will melt in about 90 seconds out of the freezer, so you have to be really on your toes to get it in the kids' hands at just the right moment. When we arrived, the popsicles were solidly frozen and were met with squeals of delight from my young boys.

On the property, the wait staff is alerted that one of my boys has a peanut allergy. They obviously use a great CRM (customer relationship management) program to keep track of all of these data. And they communicate through wireless earpieces, offering such advisories as "Dr. Burleson, and guests are arriving for lunch. Be alerted his son has a peanut allergy." Or the fact that their housekeeping team—dressed to the hilt in perfect maid attire and always arriving in groups of two so as to interrupt the day as minimally as possible— somehow managed to remember which bed was Ben's and that the stuffed panda bear belonged to him. No matter where that bear ended up throughout that suite, the housekeeping staff always found it and nicely tucked into bed each night at turndown service. That way, when we arrived back in the room from dinner, Mr. Panda Bear was waiting patiently, tucked into the covers and resting on Ben's pillow.

Sure, one could argue that at a minimum of $1,500 per night and most suites going for well above twice that amount, this company can afford to provide such amazing service. True enough. But consider for a moment that most of your patients pay you $5,000, $6,000, or $7,000 and up for a service where most of us can't remember the patient's name if we saw them in the grocery store. Nor do we coordinate a nice gift at the new patient welcome or a warm cookie during one of our patient "fond farewells" when the family leaves the building. Most of us also find it "too difficult" to customize the service to the level that your entire team is alerted to the fact that Billy, your patient, has a three-year-old sibling with a peanut allergy and should not be offered any snacks in the reception area that might contain traces of peanuts.

> *Don't shy away from the areas that may cost you a little bit of money. The return on investment from those efforts will be well worth it for the little it costs you to do it.*

Imagine what your practice would look like if you were to offer such a high level of service to your patients. Being a new concept, it may seem far-fetched or just too much to take on. But if you do take it on, you will absolutely set yourself apart from your competition. You will also give your new patients a welcome like they have never received before. You will, without a doubt, give them something they must go out and talk about. Amazing service like that is so unique and rare, they simply have to share it with everyone around them.

PUT IT INTO ACTION

Now is the time to think about what you can do to improve the way your office welcomes new patients.

- Make a list of five things you can start doing in your practice to welcome them in a big way.

- Assign each of the responsibilities to staff members so all of your ideas are implemented.
- Attach a dollar value you think adding this level of service might generate for your practice.
- Set a deadline for implementation. Make the move *now* for this to happen so that a year from now, you are benefiting from all of the new referrals it will bring to your office.

MORE ABOUT SERVICE

Doctors receive a lot of schooling and training, but very little of that education covers how to treat our patients so they will want to continue doing business with us and to refer our office to others. That's why so few doctors have figured out the best ways to achieve these results.

I have worked with many orthodontists who are wonderful at what they do, but they have not taken any measures to ensure a great patient experience. Without that, it makes it difficult for the patient to want to make another appointment or to refer the office to others.

Research has shown time and again that customers are more interested in the quality of service they receive than they are with the speed of that service. They are willing to wait a little longer if they know that the service they are going to get will be great. In other words, if you have been putting your efforts into offering *fast* service rather than focusing on *quality* service, it's time to make some changes. People want the quality service far more than they want fast service.

Along with the physical aspects that go into customer service, such as the environment and what the patient can visibly see, there is a lot of psychology behind it all, too. *Reciprocity* is a term in the field of social psychology that is good to know. Reciprocity is the positive action that someone takes after someone has done something nice for them. For example, if you do something nice for your new patient and go out of your way to make a big welcome to your office, the concept of reciprocity will kick in. Healthy-minded individuals have an innate sense that leads them to want to be even nicer in return and have

> *Healthy-minded individuals have an innate sense that leads them to want to be even nicer in return and have gratitude when someone has treated them nicely or has done something for them.*

48

gratitude when someone has treated them nicely or has done something for them. This means that psychologically, when you welcome them in a big way, you will also be helping your new patients retain positive thoughts about your office.

Let's say one day your office is running behind, and your patient is waiting in the lobby. You know it's going to be another thirty minutes before you get to him, but you can see he is getting a little agitated waiting. This is a scene that plays out in practices all over the country on a regular basis. You have two choices you can make here, and each is going to lead to a very different outcome.

On the one hand, you can let the patient know your office is running behind, apologize, and then sit back down and hope that he doesn't look toward your staff again. That's the approach most offices seem to take. If the man *does* approach the reception desk to inquire about how much longer, the staff treats him as if he must be impatient and he'll just have to wait his turn. In other words, he doesn't get a whole lot of understanding for having to sit there all the extra time. Patients realize that our time is valuable as doctors. But in turn, we must realize that their time is equally valuable, and whatever time we may be running over is being taken out of their schedules.

On the other hand, the approach you may want to take instead is to walk out to the waiting room yourself for a few seconds to nicely greet the patient. Explain to him that you had an unexpected emergency come up with a patient and it pushed your schedule back, but you always try to accommodate emergency situations. Then tell him you'd like to treat him to a Starbucks drink of his choice while he's waiting. Have one of your staff members run to Starbucks and get his favorite drink, and grab a USA Today, too. That small gesture will go a long way toward letting him know you realize you are cutting into his time and that you care about him as a patient.

Plus, making sure he's comfortable with a coffee and paper during his wait will spark the psychological reciprocity factor within his mind, prompting him to be grateful and think positively, despite the fact that he's having to put up with your office running late. Because your office didn't just brush off the delay as a mere "matter of fact"—one that he'd just have to deal with—he's much more likely to refer to your office. He will also know that if he ever has an emergency situation, that he will also get great treatment. People look favorably toward the effort you put in to make them comfortable, despite the delay.

Keep this in mind, because we always have an important choice to make when there is a delay. We can either ignore the person, acting as if our time is more valuable than theirs; or we can express our apologies and go above and beyond to try and make them more comfortable. When we are causing a problem for someone, the issue can often be smoothed out by one small act of kindness that shows we care that they are being inconvenienced and that we are doing what we can to help solve it. If we ignore the problem, we may lose the patient because of their frustration, and there is a good chance we won't get any referrals as well. Patients realize we are human and that once in a while, issues arise that we must deal with. If we handle it correctly, the patient will respect us for it, remain a loyal patient, and will absolutely go on to refer others. People appreciate businesses that handle problems appropriately and with care and concern for their customers and patients.

HOW TO ACHIEVE PRACTICE GROWTH

Think about all the things you have done to advance your career and practice. Like others in this field, you have likely spent a great deal of time, money, and attention on setting up your office, honing your skills at treatment, and advertising your services. But how much have you done toward creating relationships and wonderful experiences for your patients? Have you ever really thought about the little things you could do to wow them, to really impress them, and to set yourself apart from others?

I've worked with a lot of doctors over the years and there has been a common theme among them: they are evaluating their office and advertising and working on improving their skills to grow their business. They are working hard to advance their career and practice. But by overlooking the *patient* part of the equation, they are leaving a lot behind.

When you turn your focus to the patient and create an amazing experience for them, I guarantee you will no longer have to work very hard to advance your career or grow your practice. Those happy and impressed patients will do all the work for you. They will be the ones to advance your career as they spread the good news about your office and personality with all of their friends, family, and even strangers they meet in the store.

Instead of spending so much time directly working on advancing your career and growing your practice, turn your efforts toward your patients and let them do that work for you. Treat them like gold, and they will become your biggest cheerleader, helping to advance your career and grow your business without you even having to be in the driver's seat. You also won't have to spend a lot of money on advertising to get new patients, because they will want to tell people about you, bringing in new patients for you on a regular basis.

How does that sound as a new approach to practice marketing and growth? Give it a try and see where it takes you. If this method doesn't work, you can always go back to doing what you have been doing all along. But my guess is that once you try this, there will be no going back. You will have a cheering section for you out on the streets, pushing your practice along as your new patients grow steadily.

One of the smartest things you can do—and it doesn't cost a dime—to impress a patient is to remember their name and to call them by it. People love to hear the sound of their name, especially when they are doing business with someone. It makes them feel more appreciated and recognized. Try to use the person's name in conversations. When you do this, they immediately have a better view of you because you have identified them and taken the time to acknowledge them as a person, rather than just the next patient in line for treatment. Calling people by name is one of the easiest ways to connect. It has a big impact on the overall realtionship, but it doesn't touch your budget or create a new expense. "Catch" your employees when they greet patients by name and reward them for it.

PAYING MORE

You may be wondering how you can put all of this into action without spending additional money. As mentioned before, with a great referral system in place, you will not need to spend the type of money on advertising and marketing that you have been allocating. Rather than *you* being the one to tout your business through advertising and marketing avenues—which are usually costly—your patients will become the driving force for bringing in new patients through their referrals.

It is also important to understand that people are willing to pay more for personalized and amazing service. If they go somewhere to receive mediocre treatment that just meets their expectations, they don't expect to have to pay much. In our society, people overwhelmingly believe that you get what you pay for. If something is cheap, for example, they expect it also to be mediocre or just barely acceptable. People expect that middle-of-the-line products will meet their expectations. But when people pay a higher premium for something, they also expect the treatment to be premium. When you are providing your patients with an amazing experience unlike what they get elsewhere, they will be willing to pay more for that service.

Consumers have had all they can take with mediocre and barely acceptable service. They get that type of service on a daily basis with just about every place they do business with. Unfortunately, they have come to expect that kind of treatment. But what they really crave and what they are really impressed by are those few companies out there that offer an amazing experience, no matter what type of service they are seeking. They want a personalized experience where they feel like the business cares about whether or not they walk through that door. They want to be known by name, talked to, and understood. If you can do all that, you will be providing them with the experience that wows them and gets them talking. And that is what leads to a continuous supply of referrals to grow your practice and advance your career.

Think about the variety of things you can do to improve the experience for your new patients. Consider what you presently do with new patients, from the moment that first phone call comes in to set the appointment through the first appointment. Have you been doing things to welcome them in a *big* way? If you haven't, you can change that immediately. Decide what you will do to turn it around, share it with your staff to get everyone on board and then put it into action. Not only will your team take pride in making people feel so welcome, but your new patients will know they have made the right choice in doing business with your office.

CHAPTER FIVE

REASON #5: INADEQUATE THANKS—THEY DON'T REFER BECAUSE THEY ARE NOT THANKED ADEQUATELY AND PROMPTLY

Up until this point, we have spent a lot of time focused on the new patient. Our efforts and thoughts have gone into making sure they are happy, comfortable, and want to continue treatment with your office. During this chapter, we are going to turn our focus toward the current patient or dentist who is referring people to you. We'll look at how and why you should make the effort to show gratitude to those who refer people to your office. Now it's time to think about cultivating those referral relationships which are so important to the growth of your business and are a vital part of a successful referral system.

I want to start out this chapter with a fair warning: please do not waste too much time being offended by what you read in this chapter. Trust me when I say I've heard every excuse why your particular area is different, and the reasons why you can't send small gestures of gratitude when someone is referred to you. Believe me, I am not advocating *quid pro quo*; but you absolutely *can* send small, personal signs of your thanks when someone is referred to your practice. Fortunately, most of your competitors won't take the time to systematically implement a referral thank-you system. This puts you way ahead of them in terms of customer service and in gaining new referrals. It will also set your office apart in a good way.

Most likely you have heard about the power of having gratitude. In every area of life, when we are grateful for what we have, we end up getting more of what we want. Our focus is the same in business. Instead of focusing on what we want or don't have—such as wanting more patients—we need to change our way of thinking. We need to think about being grateful for those we have and to start expressing gratitude, which in turn will bring us more of those new patients.

AN ATTITUDE OF GRATITUDE

One of the most common reasons that patients and dentists are not referring your office is because you are not adequately thanking them—or you are not doing so promptly. Just consider for a moment how you would feel if you were helping someone and they never thanked you for that help; or the thank-you was delayed, implying that they were not all that grateful for what you had done. Would it make you more or less likely to want to continue helping them? People like to be acknowledged and thanked for doing their part in helping others.

This is not to say that everyone out there is always looking for a thank-you for sending you a referral or doing something nice for others. There are plenty of times when you just do things without looking for a response from the person you are helping. But the bottom line is that *everyone* likes feeling appreciated.

Have you ever done something for someone and they didn't thank you for it, or the thank-you that they gave you didn't feel sincere? It is something that leaves you feeling unappreciated. Your patients are the same way when they leave your office. If they are not being promptly and adequately thanked, they don't feel appreciated. They may even feel that they are just a number to your office, or that you just see them as a dollar sign. The last thing you want to do is make your patients feel like they are just another person in a long line.

In every area of life, when we are grateful for what we have, we end up getting more of what we want.

Each and every patient needs to feel as though they are appreciated and that they are important to you. This applies from the moment they are greeted, to the experience they receive while in the office, to what happens after they leave, or when they are between visits. Go out of your way to make them feel appreciated, and you will get referrals from them every time. Anyone can send a postcard on the patient's birthday. That's being somewhat thoughtful, but not all that much. I recommend taking it a step further and going all out to make them feel special.

You could focus on the patient's birthday, sending them a gift card or something special. But what would really show them your appreciation is to send them something when they first begin treatment, or when they hit a milestone with their treatment. When they have been going to your office for a few months and they get a thank-you card in the mail with a gift card to the local ice cream shop, they will feel appreciated and that you have gone above and beyond in thanking them for being a patient. Take the time to actually tell them "thank you" when you see them, too.

The bottom line is that if people are not referring their family and friends to your office, there is a reason. In order for you to fix what's wrong, you first have to determine what that reason is. These five reasons I've discussed are a great place to start. By evaluating each of them and putting them into practice—even adopting them one at a time to master them—you *will* conquer these issues, your patients will be shocked by what a great office you have and they will want to refer their friends on a regular basis.

Most companies do not have a referral system in place. If you are one of them, don't feel bad because it's not something that you have given much thought.

Now is the time to change this and make a referral system part of your marketing effort. Forget about the past and what you didn't do or didn't have in place; let's start focusing on the future and getting the referral system in place from here on out. No more wasted time—or rather, wasted money and referrals. This is where everything begins to change for the better.

KEEPING IT SIMPLE. . .OR NOT

The good thing is that when you give someone a thank-you for the referral they sent your way, it doesn't have to be elaborate. Thanking them can be as simple as a handwritten note from the doctor or treatment coordinator. These notes might include a small gift card to Starbucks or a favorite local store or restaurant. Take some time to personalize the gift and show that you care they sent you a referral. Remember, patients and dentists can refer anyone they want—even your competition—so it says a lot when they decide to refer *you*.

You'll also want to make sure you pay attention to your patient's preferences when sending them a thank-you. For example, if one of your patients is into fly fishing and hates coffee, don't send a Starbucks card. Instead, send him a little gift card to Bass Pro Shops or find him a fly fishing-themed business card holder. Try to get creative and tailor your thank-you to the referring patient.

Make it a priority to nurture the relationship. When you take the time to build relationships with these referral sources, you will strengthen their commitment to sending you even more referrals.

It's also important to send your thank-you notes and gifts promptly. This shows more excitement about the referral than letting it sit on the back burner for weeks or months before responding to say thank you. It also lets the referral source know that you are paying attention and are on top of things. Perhaps they won't send the next referral until they have gotten feedback about sending you the first one. Respond promptly and you will have a better opportunity at keeping the flow of referrals coming steadily.

When it comes to sending your referral thank-you notes, make sure you send them in the physical mail. I know email is more convenient and quicker, but it really doesn't count here. Ideally, you should get your note in the mail the very same day you discover someone has referred a new patient to you. There are many doctors who only send little notes and gifts if the referral starts treatment at their practice. You don't have to admit if you have fallen into that category. But I believe those who follow this practice are making a big mistake. It's not your referring patient's fault that you didn't get their friend or family member to say yes to treatment. Therefore, you should send a thank-you and gift *every* time, without fail, to anyone and everyone who sends you a new patient.

If you don't acknowledge the referral simply because the person they referred didn't agree to start treatment with your office, then you may or may not get another referral from them. But if you *do* take the time to show them you are grateful for the referral, there is a strong chance they will jump at the opportunity to refer your office again. Maybe it takes a couple of times before one of their referrals goes through with treatment, but it is still worth the effort and will certainly pay off in the long run.

Whether or not you keep it simple or decide to be a little more elaborate, it is entirely up to you. But put in the effort to do *something* to show gratitude to those who refer you. If you want to do something bigger, think of creative ideas, such as having a referral party once or twice per year. After sending a thank-you to those who refer you, keep track of their name on a list. Make that your guest list for your referral party, where they will be treated to a catered dinner, prizes, and a fun time. You can rent a hall or hold it at a restaurant, where the wait staff can do most of the work for you. Then all you have to do is show up, be personable, show them your fun side, and do things to build those important relationships.

When it comes to a dentist's office, you also want to send your thank-you notes. But perhaps there's an office that sends you numerous referrals. This is an office you want to show some extra gratitude toward, so be sure to do something special for them. Have a lunch catered and delivered to the entire office staff, complete with take-home goodie bags for each staff member. Inside the goodie bags, add in something like movie ticket passes with a note about treating them out to a fun evening in appreciation for their referrals.

You may be thinking that giving gifts like this is just a way of kissing their butts or brown-nosing. You can look at it that way—and if you do, then, quite frankly, you will be leaving money on the table. But I prefer to look at it more along the lines of practicing gratitude and cultivating relationships that will help to grow your practice. I hope that's the way you will think of it, too, so you can gain the benefits of implementing this into your referral system.

People like to feel appreciated and that their efforts are recognized. When you take the time to show you care about getting their referrals, they will appreciate that. Plus, consider who you would want to keep sending referrals to. Would you rather send referrals to someone who doesn't acknowledge that you sent them, or to someone who shows they are grateful for them? My guess is that you are going to send them to the doctor who shows gratitude and that they care about receiving them in the first place, rather than to someone who doesn't take the time or put in the effort to give thanks. It really takes only a small effort to thank the referral source, but the gesture stays in their mind and will end up generating more referrals for you down the road.

TRIED AND TRUE

There are some other tried-and-true methods for making great connections with those who are referring patients to you. For starters, consider creating a gift closet. In doing so, you can stack it up with books and goodies and little trinkets of appreciation that you can send quickly after a new referral comes in. This is all part of automating your referral system so you don't have to spend time trying to get these things together once the referral comes in. You will be ready to go, able to react quickly with every new referral.

If you are one of the many private clients I work with, at some point during the year, you received a box from me. It might be a few articles of interest, a book, a small gift, or a reminder of an opportunity I think you should be pursuing. I don't send everyone a typical cookie-cutter box of corporate crap from Harry and David. That screams "I cared enough to send you something, but don't really care *that* much." Try sending a corporate box of goodies with nuts and chocolates to a patient who has a severe peanut allergy and see how quickly their referrals dry up.

Instead, challenge yourself to be thoughtful and creative. Make it more personal if you can, so they can tell you took the time to actually think about them and their interests. If, for whatever reason, you insist on *not* doing this, then delegate it to one of your employees who loves to make people smile. No doubt there is someone in your office who has a knack for this type of thing and will enjoy being creative in putting together a little package to send off to those sending you referrals. Give them the freedom and guidance to generate gifts and thank-you packages that none of your competitors will take the time to implement. When you do that, you will stand out, you will be appreciated, you will get more referrals, and your office will be anything but boring.

MAKING THE CONNECTION

One of the most effective things you can do to get referrals is to work on nurturing the relationships you have with your patients and referring dentists. Again, you can do this by striving to *not* be boring. Forget being normal and playing it safe. Aim for being bold and standing out. Is one of your patients or referring dentists featured on the cover of a local magazine? Does one of them have the nicest frame shop in town? Have the one with the frame shop frame that article and then send it to the person's home or office along with a personalized note from you.

There are many ways you can stand out and make a connection with those who refer your office. Do you know the favorite hobbies of your best patients and dentists? If so (and this is easy information to find out and pay attention to), send them a birthday cake themed with that hobby or sport that they love so much.

One central theme throughout this book is that you cannot be boring and expect to get referrals. Being boring is going to cost you, and the price of it is going to be quite high. Nobody talks about boring, remembers boring, makes a connection with boring, or refers boring. Be anything but boring. Stop being boring and average. You can't afford to be boring when implementing an effective internal marketing strategy. If you want to be successful and get a lot of referrals, part of your marketing strategy must include leaving behind being average and normal. Step away from that by getting creative and bold and see just where it takes you.

Another way to make the connection with your referral sources is to become the glue. You can do this by introducing your best referral sources to each other when you have referral appreciation events. Aim to be the one who creates new opportunities and relationships for referring dentists. You want to put yourself in a position where you are seen in their eyes as the valuable person who can make great introductions for them that will end up helping their career, business, or social life.

One thing you don't want to do here is be shy and hold back. Don't be shy about doing this. Be bold about it, not boring or average. If you introduce two well-matched business owners who can work together, send a little handwritten note to both reminding each of them of the introduction and provide suggestions or a strategy on what they might be able to do together. Doing things like this is a great way to build relationship capital and mine the relationship for the mutual benefits of all parties.

> One of the most effective things you can do to get referrals is to work on nurturing the relationships you have with your patients and referring dentists.

Remember, when you do things for others, good things will also come to you. When you look out for your referral sources and help them make meaningful introductions, they will in turn be grateful to you and naturally want to send you referrals. That feeling of reciprocity kicks in, and they will want to return the favor by helping you back. Chances are you have many patients and referring dentists you could introduce to each other who could go on to build meaningful relationships that are beneficial to both parties.

When you introduce them, you also want to let them know that this is something you have put some thought into. Let them know *why* you feel they should meet. They will appreciate that you took the time to think about such things and that you are also looking out for their interests. When you are planning your referral parties and events, you will want to keep this in mind so you can make it a priority to be the glue that introduces these parties. Your staff can also assist you with this as they may know some things about each of your referral sources that you haven't yet learned. They can be quite perceptive and can sometimes see where some good matches may be beneficial.

For years, Johnny Carson was the glue for lots and lots of movie deals, interview opportunities, partnerships, and joint ventures. A lot of people wanted to know Johnny for this very reason, not just because he was funny and a celebrity. They knew that there was a good chance he would introduce them to someone who would be beneficial to their lives or business. He knew everyone and everyone knew and respected him. Countless movies and media ventures might not have happened without the relationship capital that he built in Hollywood.

Find a way to become like Johnny Carson when it comes to being the glue that brings people together. Put yourself in that position in your market and invest significant energy toward nurturing long-lasting relationships. Without that effort, you're just another orthodontist all alone in your silo. You need to make it a goal to get out and move around. And while you do so, see what you can see and help everyone you can help. When you help others, in the long run, you will also be helping yourself.

RECOGNITION PAYS

Your referral system is something that you want to get your whole team involved in. They are often the eyes and ears when you are not there. They are often the first to learn about where referrals come from—or maybe even which one of your patients or referring dentists is a football fanatic. Don't let all of that information be wasted. Get them involved and encourage them to contribute to taking care of your referring patients and doctors in an interesting way that will get you more referrals.

Encourage your team to get in the habit of paying prompt compliments to each other. Our employees use "Caught ya!" certificates when they catch someone going above and beyond. They are usually accompanied by a $20 bill and a reminder that lunch is on us today. But the real purpose is prompt recognition and a reward for doing the right thing. You know what happens when you implement a system like this, one that rewards them for doing great things? It gets people to do even more great things. After a while, your team will be identifying those who need to be acknowledged right away. It will become like second nature to them, and it will benefit the entire office.

Another thing we do at my practice is publish an entire newsletter every month just for our employees. This newsletter is basically a big "Look what awesome stuff so-and-so did this month." Our team loves it and always looks forward to reading it each month. It is mailed to their home so they can share it with their family, and they appreciate the recognition they get for doing great things on behalf of our team and reaching our company goals.

Your patients are no different. They all want to be thanked promptly, even if they say they don't really need the recognition. Everyone wants to be recognized. If you doubt this fact, you've never seen the Oscars, Grammys, or MVP awards after a major sporting event. Even grown adults want recognition and awards. Getting your employees in the habit of complimenting and thanking each other is a strong step toward building the habit of doing it to the patients. By training them to look for the good and finding ways to show recognition inside the office, they will do it with your patients and referring dentists, too. It's something that becomes second nature after you do it for a while. That's when your referral system has moved one step closer to being automated, making your job easier, and bringing in a steady stream of referrals.

THOSE WHO REFER

Both your patients and the dentists who are in your area are key components of your successful referral system. By taking care of your patients and treating them in a manner that is far above and beyond what your competitors are doing, you are bound to get referrals. By going out of your way to not be boring and to let your patients see you in a relaxed atmosphere from time to time, you will build relationships. Community building starts with the relationships you forge with your patients and your referring doctors.

When you take the time to thank your referring sources, you are showing everyone that you are grateful for all that comes your way. Many books have been written on the importance of gratitude and its life changing effects. When you express gratitude, you are also sharing kindness. Albert Schweitzer advised that we all train ourselves never to delay or neglect our expression of gratitude. In doing this, he believed that we wouldn't be taking things for granted, because nothing done for us would be accepted as a matter of course.

Albert was absolutely right. If you get referrals and don't immediately acknowledge the person who took the time to refer someone to you, then the message you are sending is that you have taken those referrals for granted, that you feel it's just a matter of course. The truth is anything but that. In order to be successful, have an effective referral system, and grow your practice the way you dream of doing, you cannot take anything for granted. And you must not ever think that getting referrals is a matter of course.

Every referral you receive from someone is a gift, even if the person doesn't end up agreeing to treatment through your office. It's a gift of trust on the behalf of the referral source. They believed in you and your team enough that they suggested people call your office. Think about how many other practices in your area they could have suggested—or they could have not suggested anyone at all. But they chose *you*, and they did so for a reason. They believe in you and your team. Show them some gratitude in return, and there's no doubt that the relationship will strengthen and the referrals will continue to come.

PARTY PLEASING

I mention several times in this book that having a party is beneficial. In fact, when it comes to taking care of your biggest fans who refer you the most, it's a must. There are a number of good things that can result from doing something like this. Even keeping your party to a select ten to twenty people will have some major benefits.

When planning the party, be selective about whom you will invite. Have your team consider who your top patient referrers are and start with that as your list. This can be a mix of referring patients, dentists, or even a blogger in the area who sends you a lot of traffic. Your list is going to be made up of those who consistently send you referrals. You may also want to consider a few people who *could* become consistent referral sources. Perhaps those people have sent you a few, but you can see there is potential to get many more if you work on strengthening that relationship.

You may also want to consider holding an educational event. Invite referring dentists—or referring hygienists—and give them a chance to learn something new while they are there. The party can also be a thank-you, but they will go home with new knowledge as well. The reason why events like this work so well is because they provide an opportunity for human bonding. You will be able to work on relationships that are often difficult to strengthen because you rarely ever see them face-to-face. Additionally, by having these events or parties, you will further establish yourself as an expert or authority on the topic to those in attendance.

> One key to keeping these events exciting is to treat them as if they are exclusive events.

One key to keeping these events exciting is to treat them as if they are exclusive events. And in many ways they really are exclusive, since you are carefully hand-picking who will be in attendance. Once your guests arrive, keep in mind that you will want to take the time to speak with each one of them. Everyone will want a few minutes with you by themselves, and they deserve to get that as well. This is also an opportunity for you to consider who you can introduce to each other so that you become the glue. If you play your cards right and put some thought into the strategy of your event or party, you will see many benefits as a result.

Your event can be an educational experience, a fun party, or it can be something altogether different. You can get creative with it and put something together that is exciting and that people will want to attend. They will walk away feeling good about having spent their time networking with you and the others from the community. You will know you have created a successful event when it's over and people begin to thank you for being invited. They realize you could have invited everyone and will be grateful they made it to your short list of invites.

Keep in mind that you are not having these events so you can do a hard sell to those who attend. You selected these people to attend because they already know your services and they refer you to others. There's nothing wrong with having some take-home info or a book to give to them, but don't spend your time selling anything other than your personality. You want to take this time to focus on building relationships with those who came and letting them know you are grateful for the referrals they send your way.

A WORD ABOUT GRATITUDE

As you can see by now, I'm big on expressing gratitude and in expressing it in big ways. I adopted an attitude of gratitude many years ago, and I know that it's made a huge difference in my life. There is also plenty of research supporting the many benefits of expressing gratitude and being grateful for all you have, rather than focusing on what you don't have.

Not only will you end up getting plenty more referrals when you express gratitude for the referrals you do get, but there are other benefits as well. By expressing gratitude, research suggests that you will likely end up being someone who exercises regularly, feels better about his life, is more optimistic, has more alertness and enthusiasm, and is more determined. There is also a good chance you will have more energy, sleep better, and much more. Some studies have even suggested that having an attitude of gratitude helps to protect people from certain diseases, such as coronary heart disease.

Just imagine how you and your team will benefit by making gratitude a priority. Not only will you see growth in your referrals and the amount of business that your practice does, but you will also benefit in other ways, both personally and professionally. The act of being grateful is going to create an office atmosphere where people are more supportive of each other, there is a positive energy, and the patients feel good being there. There are so many benefits to expressing gratitude, there is a good chance you will wonder why you haven't adopted such an office atmosphere much sooner.

PART II

PRACTICAL STRATEGIES
FOR BUILDING
YOUR PROFESSIONAL
REFERRAL SYSTEM

CHAPTER SIX
GETTING STARTED—
WHY MOST SMALL BUSINESSES DON'T
HAVE A REFERRAL SYSTEM IN PLACE AND
HOW YOU CAN DO THE OPPOSITE

I'VE WORKED WITH MANY DOCTORS OVER THE YEARS. I'VE LEARNED ABOUT WHAT THEY DO for their marketing, what works and what doesn't, and where improvements can be made. I've also seen firsthand how neglected their referral system is— largely because it doesn't even exist. This is because most doctors assume that every patient has the ability to make a good referral to their practice. Yet that is not the reality of the situation at all.

In reality, most of your patients do not know how to effectively talk about your office in a way that would lead a new prospective patient to actually call and seek out your services. Just as you have not been trained on how to have a referral system in place, your patients haven't been trained on the best way to refer you. But you can change that by providing them with the tools to refer you, as well as the reasons to refer. And the reasons to refer your office are important here. You have to give your patients something to talk about, or they will tend to forget about you.

Most doctors have no tools in place when it comes to helping their patients make good referrals to their practice. They continue to assume that patients will say the things that need to be said in the way they should be said, without making any effort to create a referral tool to prompt conversation, make logical arguments on their behalf, and do so effectively and efficiently—all while maintaining consistency in the message.

I've found that most small businesses will give lip service to the importance of referrals, but when the owner of the business is pressed, he or she can't answer the important questions. These questions include how many referrals they received last month and if they can list their top referrers—people who have referred three or more customers, patients, clients, or donors to their business. You should be able to show me a list of everyone who has referred at least one customer to your business.

You should know additional facts as well, including what unique demographic, sociographic, or psychographic characteristics make up this group of people. For example, in our practices, the patients who hear about us from their insurance company and were not referred by a friend or family member are only *one-third* as likely to refer someone to our practice. It's important to know this type of information so you can use it to your advantage. The more you know about exactly who is referring your office and the better you understand the people and places referring you, the more successful you will be with increasing your referrals. It is crucial to know what works for you and what doesn't so your referral efforts can be maximized to bring in more people and lead to more success.

What five things are you doing every month to stimulate new referrals?

Perhaps at this point, you haven't been doing anything. Then you have nowhere to go but up. Starting right away, make a list of five things you can do every month that will help you stimulate new referrals. Consistently do those five things every month, and you can't help but be successful—there *will* be more referrals coming into your office.

> *Most of your patients do not know how to effectively talk about your office in a way that would lead a new prospective patient to actually call and seek out your services.*

The problem is that most people never make that list and never determine what steps they want to take. They know in their mind what they should do, but they don't ever take action.

Well, that inaction will cost you every time. If you really want referrals—and since you are reading this book I think there's a good chance you do—then it is crucial that you take this step and act upon it every month.

When it comes down to it, most businesses *think* referrals are important. In fact, they *know* they are important, but they don't actually have a referral system in place. This is because *they think* it requires a lot of accurate data tracking, time, effort, and money to get the referrals.

The good news, however, is that all of the hard work and effort are absolutely worth it if you take the time to implement a referral system. Once you have the groundwork done and see the referrals that an effective system generates, then the only question you will have is why it took you so long to get on board with the idea and put it into action.

POSITIONING YOURSELF

You know you're not the only practice in town and that when people need someone in your field, they have choices. And they don't even have to stick to their own town. Many people are willing to travel a distance if they have heard that there is a great business or doctor who will be a good fit for them. It's common for people to seek businesses in larger cities—even if it means driving an hour each way—because they like the

> *Many people are willing to travel a distance if they have heard that there is a great business or doctor who will be a good fit for them.*

idea of having more options and access to what others may feel are better ones, too. This is one of the reasons it is so important that you position yourself differently.

To position your practice differently, you should think about how much most businesses interact with you after you spend money with them. Do you get a handwritten thank-you card after your first contact or purchase? Were you asked for key demographic information, such as address, email, phone, and date of birth at those businesses? Have you ever been invited to a customer appreciation party, trunk show, birthday event, or other special occasion by that business? Do the employees and sales associates of that business greet you by name when you arrive?

These are a lot of questions to ask yourself, but they are important ones and will tell you a lot about who has taken the time to position themselves differently. Your answers to these questions about most small businesses will largely be *no*.

So if that is the common experience, you and your practice must behave differently to achieve exceptional results. You need to do things that will set you apart and differentiate you from everyone else offering the same services you do in your area.

OBSERVING OTHERS

You can learn a lot about what you like and don't like in a practice by observing what others are doing. Start making a list of all the things you observe other businesses and doctor's offices do—or what they're *not* doing—and do the opposite. Having this list gives you a great starting point for knowing what you should or shouldn't be doing in your own practice. If, for example, your doctor's receptionist doesn't greet you by name, make it a point to hire someone as a greeter who is great with people and has a knack for learning and memorizing names. These people are out there, and they are worth their weight in gold.

You may see implementing this advice simply as an added expense that you don't want to take on. You are correct that it is going to take some money in order to get someone like that hired or to do some of the things that you notice need to be done in your office. But it's an investment in your office, in your patients, and in the future success of your practice. In all honesty, you can't afford *not* do them if you want to be successful and grow your practice.

If most of the businesses you visit don't send handwritten thank-you cards after your initial appointment or when you first buy something, make it a point in your practice to do the opposite. Gestures like follow-up phone calls, referral contests, patient appreciation events, randomly giving out fun prizes, and handing out small gifts at key points in your relationship are all important. I would be willing to bet your competitors are not doing these, so you will be doing the opposite. Doing the opposite is going to get you noticed, talked about, and appreciated—which leads to more referrals.

BORING FADES

I've said this many times and I'll say it many more—people don't talk about what is boring. If going to your office is the same old boring experience and it doesn't stand out in your patient's mind, then it's not going to get talked about much afterward. People don't share information about boring. Nobody wants to listen to boring, so for the most part, it isn't discussed.

So make every effort to ensure your office is not boring. If what you are doing is boring, then you are not going to get referrals no matter what you do. This is especially important to remember when it comes to spending your hard-earned dollars on advertising and marketing. While you may be pouring money into these things, they may be falling on deaf ears if what you are putting out there is boring.

When you put out ads, promotional materials, or other types of marketing, don't spend the money without first asking if what you are doing is boring. If it is, you have to change it before purchase, or it will never give you the return on investment that will make it worth your while. If what you are putting out there is interesting, fun, and memorable, then go for it. But always track it to see if it was worth the effort or if further changes need to be made.

Always remember that vanilla only works for ice cream. You have to boldly proclaim what no one else is doing. Think of what you can offer the people in your area that nobody else is offering. Be bold when you are thinking of what that may be. What if you guaranteed braces or Invisalign without missing any work or school? Think about how that would set your office apart, make you stand out, and would put you in a class all your own. Just think about how many people that would bring in through your door and how many referrals you would get from that. People don't want to miss work or school for their appointments. If you offer that service to them, you will be providing a solution to a problem they simply can't turn down.

REMEMBER TO ASK

Most people don't give a second thought to referrals. They don't realize just how important they are to small businesses. In fact, most small businesses also don't remind their customers frequently enough that referrals are the lifeblood of their operation. You know that you need referrals, but there is a good chance you are not conveying that message to your patients so they can support you in your efforts.

It's important to remember that when braces go on, when braces come off, or when patients get a new retainer, you have the opportunity to remind them your small business needs referrals. Look for any excuse to remind patients that you would love to help their friends and family. After all, that's why you went to school for so long, isn't it? To help people? It seems to me you would want to tell as many people as you can about your office.

REMINDING WORKS

There are a variety of ways you can go about reminding your patients that you appreciate referrals. You can get creative with it, too. In-office signage that thanks them for referrals and lets them know you appreciate them works. So, too, does having information and signage at events and putting it in your newsletter and on your surveys. Try to do it at every opportunity you get. It's always a good time to remind patients that you appreciate referrals.

Segment your list and concentrate your efforts. If you have patients who have referred new patients to you in the past, they should always be on the top of your list to invite to events and to participate in your next referral contest. Not all patients will refer, but the ones who do will often refer three, four, five, or more patients to your practice. Find centers of influence and then keep those people in mind every time you do something special so you can reach out to them and get those people involved.

In nearly every other aspect of life, discrimination is bad, but not when it comes to marketing. That's how you tap into your most valuable patients and maximize your referral potential rate. Weight your efforts with patients who are centers of influence. If you're treating a school teacher, small business owner, dental hygienist, or someone who is in front of a lot of people (think sports celebrity or newscaster), then you have a tremendous opportunity to make sure that patient knows you appreciate their referrals.

Think about those patients who have the ability to reach a lot of people. As they are in a position to meet a lot of people, they may be able to refer your office many times. Consider if any of your patients are teachers, small business owners, health writers, or even local bloggers who cover health topics. These people can be a collective gold mine when you begin to narrow them down and tap into what they are capable of in terms of helping you with referrals. To get serious about having continual referrals coming into your office, you have to take the time to build on this list, and then work the list so that it works for you.

REPEAT THE PROCESS

What I have found from speaking with many other doctors in the field is that they are not consistent with their referral efforts. They may work on it in spurts; but as soon as some referrals come in from their efforts, they tend to back down. When this happens, things slow down; and they assume that the referral strategies and efforts are not working. But that's because they stopped working the strategies and putting in the effort, not because the referrals themselves just dried up.

> It's a good idea for people to see your message more than once. . .it takes a consumer seven times of seeing your message before it resonates and they take action.

Most small businesses that carve out a little bit of time for referrals will often stop working on it when they get back into the daily grind month after month. But you know better than to take this approach. You must stay focused on referrals and continue to repeat anything that is working—and even ramp it up. The minute one of your patient appreciation events or referral contests or newsletter inserts takes off like wildfire, you have a moral duty and obligation to your practice and its vision to leverage that win and ramp it up. It's not the time to back down, run the other way, or get too comfortable. That will cause you to pass up this opportunity. Rather, you want to do it again and keep that momentum going strong.

Don't rest on your laurels, and don't assume everyone got the message the first time around. If it worked once, it will likely work again and again. If it stops working, change the format and mix it up a little bit. Don't assume everyone is paying attention to every promotion you run and every event you hold. Sometimes just coming back to the same group of people with the same offer will get you an even bigger response from the people on the list who weren't really paying attention the first time around.

REPETITION HELPS

It's a good idea for people to see your message more than once. In fact, there are plenty of industry experts who believe in the Theory of Seven—the idea that it takes a consumer seven times of seeing your message before it resonates and they take action. There are numerous reasons why this happens, including the fact that it's a noisy market and timing is tricky. If your marketing message is lost in the shuffle, then that noisy market is going to keep you from standing out. Your mission is to find a way to stand out if you are in a busy market.

Also, just because someone has been exposed to your marketing message a couple of times, it doesn't mean they are ready for the service at that moment. Nobody thinks about hiring a good plumber, for example, until something actually goes wrong with the plumbing. If your message is reaching people who are not yet ready for your services, then it will almost always be overlooked. But the next time they see your marketing message—or maybe four or five times down the line—they may be ready or know someone who is. Timing makes a difference when it comes to reaching your target market.

Consistency is key when it comes to getting new referrals, whether you are marketing your practice or working with your highest producing referral sources. Being consistent with your efforts will always pay off in the long run. The problem arises when people are not consistent and they put in minimal, intermittent efforts. Having new referrals coming in spurts or waves is not going to benefit your practice as much as keeping a steady stream of them rolling in all year long. You want the steady stream of referrals coming your way so you can maximize your office's potential. Plus, each of those new referrals has the potential to become your next big referral source.

EVEN WHEN IT HURTS

One of the core things that people know about me is that I don't sugar-coat things. In fact, there are many other doctors who find me offensive because I tell the truth, even when it hurts. Even if the facts are painful or the B.S. is all over the place, I'm the one guy who will cut through it all to show you the truth. I believe this is the best way to be. My honesty is going to save you time and help you make more money. I'm not about just giving lip service to make people feel better about what they are doing—or what they are *not* doing. I've provided consulting services to plenty of doctors who are shocked at my straight-forward approach, only to have them thank me later for how that information and approach helped kick them into the right gear.

Sometimes the truth hurts, and people don't often like to hear it in this profession. But I have no problem sharing the truth with others, because I believe it will motivate and lead people in the right direction. For starters, getting more certifications or honing your clinical skills will not make you rich. I have seen many doctors go for more and more credentials to hang on their wall, hoping to bring in more patients and be able to make more money. The stark reality is that you don't need more credentials to hang on the wall, unless they are ones that thank people for referrals or invite them to a referral party. Papers on the wall will not make you more money. What *will* make you more money is having a stellar referral system in place that you consistently use. It just doesn't get any more clear-cut than that.

Furthermore, doing good work is not going to be enough. You can be the best doctor in your entire area, but if people don't know about you, you won't grow your practice or get more referrals. You have to put in the effort to bring in referrals in order to put those good skills to use.

A key concept that every doctor must realize is that they are in the marketing business. It doesn't matter so much what your services are if you don't take the time and put in the effort to properly market them. Marketing is the only way you will have the level of success that you want in your practice. Rather than spending time adding more certifications to your wall, put in the time to set up an effective referral system and market your practice properly. When you do that correctly and consistently, everything else will fall into place.

And don't worry about whether your approach makes a few enemies along the way. Trust me when I say that I've made my share of them. You have to keep in mind that if you are not attracting some complaints along the way, you are not doing enough. Those who do nothing and fly below the radar make no enemies, but they also go unnoticed and don't end up with a lot of people who really love what they are doing. You have to stand out, make some noise, and be noticed in order to make both enemies and friends. Be brave enough to do this. After all, your practice is relying on you.

> *If you are not attracting some complaints along the way, you are not doing enough.*

WHAT'S YOUR GUARANTEE?

I am a firm believer that you must have something you can guarantee in your business. If you can't guarantee satisfaction or your results, get out of the business. This is what people want and need; and if you can't consistently give it to them, then there's no reason to hang around. Do what you need to do to get to the point where you can offer a guarantee and stand behind it. People will respect it and know that you must believe in what you are providing in order to offer the guarantee.

Ask yourself what type of guarantee would make you feel comfortable when you visit a doctor's office. How would you feel if you spent thousands of dollars, only for the doctor to say that they hope it works as planned—and if it doesn't work, they're sorry but there's nothing they can do? Would you want to go back to a place that didn't unequivocally stand behind its work? Chances are, you don't want to go to a place like that for treatment, and neither do others in your community. Give them a guarantee, and I promise that information will get around as people refer your office to others.

Make a list of the things that you *can* guarantee. Determine what will make a difference to your patients, and then offer it. Every patient wants to be guaranteed that they will have a pleasant experience with your office. They also want to be guaranteed that you will do everything you can to help them achieve great results. When you stand behind your services, your patients will trust you and want to refer you to others. Referrals have a lot to do with the relationships that we build with the patients and referring sources that we have. When they both trust and like you, they will want to take the time to refer you to others.

THINKING REFERRALS

Since you are reading this book, I'm going to go out on a limb and say that you haven't yet had the referral mindset that you should have. Reading this book is a great first step, because you are taking the steps to change that. One thing you will need to develop is a referral mindset, which likely means changing the way you were thinking before so you can begin thinking in terms of referrals.

To get into the referral mindset, it's important to remember that referrals are always going to be your most cost-effective route to obtaining new patients. When you focus on having an effective referral system, you will be maximizing your profit potential and keeping other expenses down. There are a lot of ways to get your name out and get noticed, but you have to compare how much they cost to the expense of creating and maintaining an effective referral system. It will cost you money to get out information to a lot of people through such routes as seminars and advertising space. But what will it cost to get someone to refer your practice to their friend or family member?

If you do it correctly, you *will* have some costs associated with having a successful referral system in place. But if you do it right, those expenses will be *less* than having a big advertising budget. The goal with a referral system is to get other people—namely your patients and referring doctors—to talk about you. With advertising, you are

> *Building a relationship with your patients is the best way to create a mutual trust.*

essentially talking about yourself. If you do a cost analysis, you will find that it's much more expensive to talk about yourself than it is to get others to talk about you and your practice. Plus, people trust word-of-mouth referrals more than they do commercial advertising. With word-of-mouth referrals, people are hearing about you from people whose opinions they trust; and that can only strengthen their commitment to setting up an appointment with you.

Make it your goal to find out your cost per referral. At the same time, track your cost per lead that comes in from other sources, such as advertising and any direct mail efforts. Using this information, you can compare the two to see which is more cost-effective. You can also ask yourself which one will better provide you with patients who walk in the door already having a sense of trust for your office, as opposed to ones who come to your office with no idea what to expect. Remind yourself of the benefits of them having a sense of trust for you. Referrals, including their future ones, are based upon the relationships you create with people.

It's also important to consider how you can leverage relationships to your advantage. I've had people tell me they don't care for this idea because they feel like they are using people to see what they can get out of them. So what? Do you want to grow your practice or not? If you do, then you have to look for opportunities to leverage new referrals. Believe me, many of the people you know are doing the same thing with you, even if you are not aware it's taking place.

Building a relationship with your patients is the best way to create a mutual trust. This is a win-win situation because they want to trust their doctor, and you want them to trust you as a professional and to refer you because they have that trust. People only refer those they trust.

To have a referral mindset, it is also important to realize that it takes a systematic approach. Your system needs to be comprehensive, rather than just focusing on one aspect or one particular approach. Your goal is to reach your top referrers, build trusting relationships, and then remind them that you truly appreciate their sending referrals your way. You should always be in referral mode, which includes routinely thinking about new ways to generate them, and always being ready to ask people for them.

Another important part of having the right referral mindset is to believe that they *will* come. You need to believe that you'll get referrals. Our thoughts are powerful and can lead our actions and direct our reality, so it is important to believe you will get referrals—to expect to get them. When you have that mindset, you will greatly increase your chances of bringing in referrals and looking for opportunities to do so.

You also have to realize that your patients want to come to your office because they've been referred by someone else. Most people do not want to open up a phone book—or do a quick Google search—and blindly pick a doctor based on the results of their search. That tells them nothing about your integrity and quality of service. But if they can hear about you from a friend, co-worker, or someone else they know, they will feel better about the appointment. They won't be going in totally blind, having no clue of what to expect.

You like to get referrals when you need to see a new professional, and so do your patients and potential patients. When you have a referral mindset, it is a win-win situation for everyone. Not only are you helping your business to grow and be more prosperous, you are giving patients a trusted way to find a doctor. One thing that just about everyone despises are cold calls. This goes for those looking to have treatment, too. They don't want to make cold calls, or for you to make cold calls, to get the services they need.

Your mindset has to be on referrals all the time if you want to be successful. You have to want referrals, think referrals, look for opportunities to get referrals, and believe they will come to you. When you can consistently do that and continue taking action to strengthen your referral system, you will succeed at getting the ongoing referrals you both want and need.

CHAPTER SEVEN

THE TOP 10 STRATEGIES USED TO ENCOURAGE REFERRALS— WHAT TO SEND AND HOW TO SEND IT

There are many great options when it comes to encouraging your patients and dentists to give you referrals. It's good to try a variety of methods because you never know which one will resonate with each patient. Trying multiple approaches will give you a nice referral pool with people coming from various current patients and dentists. Remember that not everyone who sees your message makes the connection the first or second time, or they may not be ready at that moment. But if you remain consistent with your referral system efforts, your office and message will continually be available to people when they do need your services.

I have tried many different things in my practice to get referrals. I have a referral mindset, as we previously discussed, so the wheels are always spinning. Because it takes reaching people in a variety of ways and through different efforts, I'm almost always willing to give anything a try.

Here are what I consider to be the top ten strategies to encourage referrals in your practice:

1. EVENTS THE CALENDAR GIFTS TO YOU

If you can't think of a promotional event or referral contest, just pick up a calendar. In the United States, there are 11 federal holidays: New Year's Day, Inauguration Day, Martin Luther King Jr. Day, George Washington's birthday, Memorial Day, Independence Day, Labor Day, Columbus Day, Veterans Day, Thanksgiving, and Christmas.

Add to this list holidays such as St. Patrick's Day, Valentine's Day, Tax Day, opening day for baseball, college football bowls, and so on; and there are many holidays and noteworthy days throughout the year that you can tie into referral parties.

At minimum, you should be doing several big events per year. At some of these events, focus on your top referrers and make the invitations exclusive to that group. If your creative team needs a few brain-stimulating ideas, look into the "Truth about Referrals Toolkit," the companion to this book. It offers scores of ideas for patient and referring dentist internal marketing campaigns that are focused on helping you boost your referrals. It is important to put holding fun events at the top of your list to have an effective referral system.

2. REFERRAL CONTESTS

People love winning things. Throughout the year, you should hold random raffle drawings in your practice that will reward patients for referrals and their continued trust and confidence in your office. If there is one thing people don't like, it's to enter into contests and then they never hear anything about those who won. Be sure to take the time to show off the winners on all of your social media channels, as well as on your website, in your practice newsletter, and in your monthly employee newsletter.

You want to open the contest to every patient, so give each of them some referral cards. Encourage them to enter the contest and be sure to let them know what they could win. If you make it seem like the contest is an exciting event for your office, they will see it that way, too.

These contests could be seasonally-themed events, or they could be associated with a charity or some other cause that deserves attention. For example, each year we pair up with Smiles Change Lives, and we commit to treating one patient through that charity for each person who starts comprehensive orthodontics care during the month of October.

In the last three years, we've committed to treating over 500 patients through this program. Referrals from our patients who own businesses or are leaders in their places of worship will often refer someone for Smiles Change Lives, in addition to referring several other patients who are self-pay. There's nothing wrong with helping out a great cause while at the same time boosting your referrals through goodwill.

3. PROMPT AND COURTEOUS
THANK-YOU AFTER THE REFERRAL

When you get a referral from someone, what do you do to thank the person who gave the referral? If you said nothing, you are not alone. Many people don't think to do anything to thank the referring person. But if you do, you can count on getting referrals from them again in the future. When they receive a special thank-you, they will want to refer you again because they feel good about the first referral. People like to be acknowledged for their efforts. Consider keeping a stash of gift cards for some local restaurants that you can send in a thank-you card. Include a little handwritten note that says you appreciate the referral and would like to send them to lunch on your office. Oftentimes, the next referral comes quicker if you simply write a prompt and courteous thank-you card for each referral.

How many times have you referred someone to a business and never received a thank-you card for your referral? Likely, the answer is that you didn't receive one from the business owner. If you had, statistically you would be much more likely to refer again. This simple act of sending prompt and courteous thank-you notes has been a large part of our practice growth over the years.

4. GREETING PEOPLE BY NAME

I've heard every excuse in the book for why doctors resist my advice on learning and memorizing patient names. You could think up new excuses that I've never heard of and repeat them until you are blue in the face, but that doesn't change the fact that if I remember a patient's name and greet them by name at the grocery store or little league field—and when their parent notices me doing that—I just earned big time bonus points, and likely a referral as well.

Granted, I don't remember them all by name, but I do remember a great deal of them. Keep in mind that I have over 11,000 active patients. You can't blame it on practice size and you can't blame it on cognitive ability. I'm a country bumpkin from Southern Ohio who can barely string together a coherent sentence. I'm not the smartest guy on the planet. You don't have to be either if you put intentional effort and focus into remembering your patients by name. Think about this—what name does everyone on the planet love the most? The answer is their own name. Start using it as part of your overall referral strategy.

5. PATIENT NEWSLETTER

I've heard a number of excuses for why doctors don't send out patient newsletters. Many have told me that newsletters are dead, their patients don't read them, they don't have the time for them, etc. These are just some of the excuses I hear from doctors. But they miss a fundamental concept—and so do you—when you fail to communicate at least monthly with your patients. The relationship with your list of patients is the most valuable asset in your practice. Very few doctors realize this, but those who do will be highly successful. Patients assume you're going to give them a great, new smile, fix their functional problems, improve their TMJ pain, or help their child with cleft lip and palate. None of that is going to earn you referrals. Going beyond the deliverable and building a relationship with patients who are interested to see where you vacation, to see what you do in your free time, to read about fun stories from your team and other patients—those are the things that help you build relationships with your patients.

> **The relationship with your list of patients is the most valuable asset in your practice.**

I routinely work with other doctors, so when they're using newsletters, I end up hearing the feedback about them. Those who use newsletters as I suggested end up discovering that they *do* work—and oftentimes in a big way.

There is one doctor I know who started putting out a newsletter for her patients, and she decided to do something a little different. She added a baking recipe in each one; each of the recipes came from her grandmother's recipe box. As it turns out, her patients loved those recipes. As a result, she has gone on to create a nonprofit bakery that supports dental mission trips, all from the simple realization that patients really did love her grandmother's recipes just as much as she did. She tells me that this little column in her newsletter is one of the biggest word-of-mouth referral sources her practice has.

Of course, I encouraged her to appropriately size and strategically place the recipes in the newsletter layout so they can easily be cut out and kept in a recipe box. Plus, it was designed so that the back of the recipe card had a little promotional piece for the practice with a fun quote about cooking from Julia Child, along with the practice's phone number and website. These recipes are often kept for years, serving as a reminder of their relationship with their orthodontist.

Another doctor I work with has gotten really creative with her newsletters and has tapped into the love the country has for their pets. One of her most popular newsletter columns is written from the point of view of her dogs. This is a neat little newsletter trick that warms the hearts of her readers. After all, people love dogs; and they love to see what kind of dog you have and what it's been up to. It may seem silly to have a column from the dog's perspective, but again this doctor also tells story after story to me about patients who have heard about her puppies and what they're up to in this month's newsletter. It's a segment of the newsletter that people can relate to; it interests them and gives them a way to feel connected to your office.

As I've pointed out many times before, referrals are largely about relationships. People need to feel they know and trust you, and that there is some kind of relationship there. When you have that, they will refer you over and over.

Consider what unique column or personal touch you can add to your newsletters that will not only set them apart from others, but make them interesting, make people want to share them, and let some of your personality shine through so your patients begin to feel like they know you.

One more point about newsletters: make them count. Make sure you send them out full of useful information. According to research, only around a third of the people you send email newsletters to are even going to open them. And fewer than that will act upon anything in there. To get a higher read rate, be sure to send out quality content and have a good headline that will entice them to open the email. Inside the newsletter, add a button or link that makes it simple for the reader to "forward to a friend." Just having that small prompt will help provide the tool needed to refer you to another person.

If you consistently put good information in your newsletter rather than just using it as an overt advertising message for your services, you will have a higher open and read rate, and your patients will be more likely to pass that information on to others.

6. IN-OFFICE SIGNAGE

We are a culture that responds to visuals, so take advantage of that by using them in your office. Visible reminders are needed everywhere in your practice. They should be focused on asking patients to participate in your referral contest or patient appreciation events. Don't assume anyone knows or cares about the referral activities going on in your practice until you show them what's in it for them. Everyone loves to win something, so when they see what they have the opportunity to win, they will take notice and become interested in referring your office.

In addition to the feedback I've gotten from the doctors I work with, I have personal experience with in-office signage well. I use visible reminders of referral contests in my office. For one of our contests, we had a promotional banner up and some signage in the office about my cleft palate foundation. The signage informed people about all of the work we do for cleft palate patients.

Because I'm highly engaged with cleft palate care, I assume everyone else already knows this about me. Well, one of our best referring dentists saw the sign and said, "I didn't know you did cleft palate care."

I laughed out loud from being caught by surprise. "How did he *not* know that?" I thought to myself.

The answer is easy, really. He didn't care about it until I showed him how it benefits him. That month, he saw a sign that reminded him that choosing my practice for orthodontic care was simultaneously choosing a provider who makes a difference in our community. That's something he liked a lot. It didn't matter to him if I did cleft palate care or not. What mattered was that he saw something that resonated with him.

This is the objective of in-office signage. You want to remind people that what you are doing is important, fun, special, and relevant to them.

It's easy to assume that people know what you do to help your community, or things that they should know about your office. That's because you are there in your office each week. But you have to remember that they are not, so they are probably not as aware of certain aspects of your practice as you may think they are. Take the opportunity to get the information out there so people know. Given the information, there is a good chance they will want to support what you are doing.

7. SOCIAL MEDIA AWARENESS

Many people who need services today begin their search online, often using social media. Since social media is a popular way referrals are made, keeping your message consistent is important. That means you should have someone dedicated to taking care of your social media pages so there is consistency across all platforms. Being able to post information and answer questions will go a long way toward getting your name out there.

For example, if someone posts a question on your Facebook page asking about a procedure, you should be ready to respond with carefully-selected, accurate information. Also, if a current patient posts good feedback, you should thank them and post a link in case they have friends and family who would also be interested in learning more about whatever type of treatment they are receiving. Since Facebook users' posts and comments usually show up in their personal newsfeed, their friends may see your response as well.

Let me be direct in saying that if you are going to play in social media, you have to jump *all* the way into the pool. Don't set up a Facebook fan page, Pinterest page, or Instagram feed and then never do anything to monitor it or keep it active and engaging. You have to keep in mind that patients ask questions, post comments, and leave feedback— sometimes positive, sometimes not so positive—on these sites, and you must be prepared to respond promptly.

> *Since social media is a popular way referrals are made, keeping your message consistent is important.*

When people praise you on social media, thank them publicly, but also send them a little gift card from Starbucks with a handwritten note. Never send an e-card or digital thank-you when a physical card in the mail will make a bigger impact—which is almost always. If you don't see why I'm saying this, try sending your mom an e-card for Mother's Day and send your spouse one for your anniversary. I think you will agree that e-cards are simply not the same as the real thing.

Social media doesn't have to be entirely online either. You can boost the social response and good behavior of your best social followers by adding some physical direct mail into the mix. Just don't forget to respond quickly and often to the online posts. The half-life of social media is far too short to let anything sit for days or weeks. When it comes to social media, you have to make the commitment to do it *right* if you are going to do it at all.

When you are using social media, the last thing you want to do is constantly push your office and services. People will tune that out after a while because they will tire of just straight sales messages. While you may want to make people aware of the various services you offer, those should not dominate your social media newsfeed. Mix in information about services with things that will engage people who follow you, such as useful tips, braces-friendly recipes, information about what is going on in your office, patient success stories, and cute memes that your target audience can relate to. Be sure also to post news about any charity work you do or ways you help the community. Also include special events, referral contests, and fun facts about your office.

Social media can be great for engaging people, spreading the message, and getting new referrals. But this is only true if it's done right. Make the commitment to either go all the way with it or skip it entirely, so it doesn't become a detriment to your office by getting started and then not being managing properly. One thing people often fail to remember is that social media is about being *social*. Interacting with those who like or follow you is a given; it is the nature of the medium. Someone in your office needs to be on it, being social with people who are engaged and willing to interact.

8. PATIENT SURVEYS

If you are like most doctors I work with, you only survey your patients at the beginning and end of their treatment. This is a typical route that doctors take, but taking this approach means you are doing what everyone else is doing—and you could be doing it a lot better. Personally, I recommend surveying patients throughout treatment; somewhere around every six months in orthodontic treatment is sufficient. It's also a good idea to survey them when adding a new service, new doctor, new location, or new hours and days for the office. These are perfect times to survey your patients, giving you an opportunity to gather important information about their experience with your office.

The surveys can serve several different purposes, including getting feedback on current performance, getting suggestions for future services and offerings, and reminding patients of things you are already doing. I like the third category the most because, again, most people don't know everything you are doing or involved with, and they don't know that you're both open to and welcome more referrals. Most people don't mind filling out surveys; and many enjoy the process of being able to give their two cents in providing feedback, so don't feel as though you are bothering them with the survey.

> I recommend surveying patients throughout treatment; somewhere around every six months in orthodontic treatment is sufficient.

Use the survey to your advantage by making sure it is going to serve one of the purposes I mentioned above. Don't waste time, money, and effort putting out a survey before you've determined its purpose. Know what you want from the survey so that you ultimately get something beneficial from it. A good survey design takes all of this into consideration. Think through your design, questions, and timing in order to get the most out of the effort people exert to fill it out.

I've given my patients many different surveys over the years, and I'm often surprised with the things I learn from them. If you take the time to review the survey responses, you will find valuable information in some of them that you can use to better your office and make improvements to the way things are done.

One of the surveys I gave my patients came back with the suggestion to get better WiFi in our reception area, make better magazines available, and create a space for the kids to do their homework. All of these are strong features of our reception area now and have prompted countless comments of praise and referrals from busy parents. But what is interesting is that these were areas we weren't really paying any attention to prior to the survey. Once these issues were brought to our attention through the survey, we took action to make improvements. As a result, not only did the patients who made the suggestions benefit, but everyone did. It ultimately created a better atmosphere for our office for all our patients to enjoy.

While you want to read what the surveys say, you also want to take the responses with a grain of salt. Don't take the feedback personally: pick and choose what feedback you want to use in your practice. Take those things that make sense and go with them, but don't worry about trying to please everyone and address every suggestion. I've learned over the years that I cannot respond to every piece of patient feedback; and there are always going to be some people who will never be completely satisfied, despite our best efforts. I've learned that even if I were open 24 hours, seven days per week, and all services were free, there would still be some people who would find fault with how we operate and would want even more.

You get to decide which actions you take as a result of your surveys. But never forget that the surveys should be used as a tool to remind your satisfied patients that you want and appreciate more referrals.

9. EMAIL AUTOMATION CAMPAIGNS

Ideally, you want to nurture the relationships you have with patients. Consistent nurturing is hard to do, however, especially because some patients prefer to read, while others prefer to watch video or listen to audio to get answers to their questions from your practice before, during, and after treatment. Customer Relationship Management (CRM) automation software, such as InfusionSoft, does a brilliant job at custom tailoring the relationship nurturing with email, direct mail, phone calls, etc., so that every patient gets exactly the level of communication that is appropriate for him or her. For example, patients who have filled out a survey are asked to attend our patient board of directors meetings each quarter where we ask our top referrers exactly what they need from the practice, what they love, and what they want to see changed. And we get to share what's on the horizon for our expanding and growing practices.

Patients who have not yet filled out our survey instead receive reminders to do so until they actually take the desired action. You can't do this level of customized interaction manually, which is why CRM software is so useful.

Find a way to communicate regularly with patients at the level they demand. Consumers who want more and more information can get it based on how they interact with the software. Those who prefer to be left alone, for example, can quietly get smaller amounts of information from our practice, so that the level of relationship interaction feels "just right". The software listens to the consumer and allows you to maintain the proper level of relationship interaction with all of them.

Using a variety of campaigns to reach people is the best route to take. You never know which one will resonate with people. I have a patient who had seen one of my special reports, read one of my books, and listened to an audio CD before she finally called up and scheduled a new patient exam. But even though her appointment was still a week away, she recognized me at the grocery store. We had never met before, but she was already familiar with me through the different avenues she had experienced already, including email, YouTube, our website, and finally through her mailbox with one of my reports and a book. The foundation for a relationship had already been laid before she even had her first appointment.

> **Find a way to communicate regularly with patients at the level they demand.**

There are some patients who don't need this level of communication; but for this patient, it was "just right" for her. In this case, she started her treatment on her first visit and paid in full because we had met her on her level. She was the type of person who needed a lot of information, and we provided that to her. In her survey on what fear or frustrations she experienced when choosing her orthodontist, not surprisingly she listed, "I was afraid I wouldn't get answers to my questions."

Everyone needs a different level of communication in order to feel valued, informed, and comfortable with your office. Your job is to find what that may be and then try to give it to them. Considering people all have different learning styles and prefer different ways of taking in information, approaching them from a variety of ways helps to ensure that the information is delivered in a manner that will be meaningful for them.

10. FORCED REFERRALS

There are many ways to get referrals, but this is my favorite type of referral strategy. It is what Dan Kennedy refers to as a "forced" referral, and what he and I have worked on for years to enhance, tweak, and test relentlessly in my practices. A forced referral means putting patients into a situation where they are practically *compelled* to talk about you because of the experience.

Referral appreciation events, where patients bring friends and neighbors, is one type of forced referral. They are also popular and fun, and they let people see you in a different light. People will get to know your personality more as a result of attending a party where you are mingling and having fun instead of working. The forced referral happens because to invite a friend to an event sponsored by their orthodontist, they are almost certain to talk about the orthodontist.

Another forced referral campaign is sending people a gift card on their birthdays or anniversaries. Every patient in our practice gets two brownies and a physical birthday card mailed to their house or work a day or two before their birthday. It's a forced referral because everyone will ask who sent them the gift. The reply, of course, is always, "my orthodontist, that's who." Sending balloons tied to a smoothie gift card and sending it to the child's school or adult patient's place of work is also a forced referral. You can't possibly walk back to class or back to your cubicle with a bunch of balloons and a gift card and not be asked numerous times who sent them to you.

Things like this force people to talk about you—which is a good thing. It gets your name out there, and it's a solid referral because the person is your patient. They are choosing to go to your office, so that in itself is a stamp of approval. Is it manipulative? You bet. Is it ethical persuasion and manipulation? I think so. But honestly, if you are changing lives, do you really want to limit the number of people you help? There's nothing wrong with getting people to talk about your office, especially if in the process your patient is going to feel really special because they got that gift from you.

Sometimes strategies like this work in a big way, even bigger than you may think they will. I personally know a mom who runs a marketing company who has used several of these techniques. Not only has she changed how she advises her clients, but she has also sent seventeen —that's right, seventeen!—patients to our practice who have started treatment. That seems unbelievable, but it's true, and we greatly appreciate it. This goes to show that small acts can lead to big results.

MORE STRATEGIES ABOUND

These are my top ten strategies for getting referrals, but there are plenty of others, too. You have to find what works for your office and put it into practice. Try a variety of things to see what works with people. Some people will respond to one thing, while others will not. Always strive to keep building relationships and stay on the radar of each of your patients. They need to know that you need and appreciate any referrals they can send your way.

Being awesome will also help you get referrals, and a great way for people to see that you are awesome is to give back to your community. Give people a chance to see you outside of the office, helping others and having fun

Make a list of things you'd like to start trying, and then get started with them. Track your progress to see which ones resonate with people. You will probably be surprised that some people respond to things that you never thought they would, while nobody responds to the things you assumed would be popular. There is a learning curve to discovering what works and what doesn't, but if you put in the time to figure that out, it will be well worth it when you start getting a continuous stream of referrals.

When you are first setting up your referral system, you may find it takes time, money, and effort. But once you have these things in place, maintaining them will be simple. Plus, the more referrals you get from your efforts, the more you will want to continue honing the referral system so that you can strengthen it to get more and more people calling your office.

I've worked with many orthodontists around the country, helping them put many of these strategies into place. Even the most skeptical of them eventually comes around to tell me how well these ideas are working once their system is up and running. These strategies have worked great for me, they have worked great for many other doctors I've worked with, and they will work great for you, too.

CHAPTER EIGHT
TIMING AND REFERRAL STRATEGY— WHEN TO THANK FOR REFERRALS AND WHEN TO ASK FOR MORE

RESEARCH HAS SHOWN TIME AND AGAIN THAT PEOPLE ARE MORE LIKELY TO BUY SOMETHING or make an appointment somewhere when they have been referred. Word-of-mouth referrals are not only important, but as you might now realize through reading this book, they are essential to growing your business. By and large, people trust referrals from those they know; and referrals always produce better results than any form of advertising you can do. When you have referrals, someone else is touting your company and services, rather than you touting it yourself through your advertising efforts.

Word-of-mouth encourages people to consider a brand or company more than an advertisement can do. Some experts believe that word-of-mouth accounts for up to half of all purchasing decisions that people make. It has that much influence on people, helping them to decide where to go, who to call, what to purchase.

In creating a referral system for your practice that will be effective and help your business grow, you have to consider many different angles. *Timing* and *strategy* are key components to having a referral system in place that is going to work for you. You have to know when to thank people for the referrals they have sent to you, and when it is appropriate to ask for more. If you get this wrong, you may miss out on some golden opportunities to bring people into your office. But if you get it right, you will open the door to many referrals for years to come.

PROMPT THANK-YOU MESSAGES

One of the biggest ways people mess up their referral system is by incorrectly timing their thank-you messages. If you think that it doesn't matter *when* you send the thank-you, then you think the same way as the majority—but you would be wrong. It makes a big difference when you send the thank-you and how quickly it is received.

Just imagine if you bought something today from someone and then a month later a thank-you message arrived. By that time, the excitement from the moment of the purchase would be done and gone, and the thank-you probably wouldn't have a lot of impact. In fact, it may even have a negative effect if you think they were slacking and just finally got around to sending you the thank-you. If they are going to be that slow about sending the thank-you, it might have been better for them to skip it all together so it wouldn't end up looking like they were simply taking their sweet time about sending it. The delay in sending the thank-you sends a message by itself, and it probably isn't a positive one.

Most companies do not thank their referrals promptly enough. That's just all there is to it. I know that we live in a world where we are busier than ever before. We seem to get ourselves working on a dozen things at one time, and we have a list as long as our arm of all the things we need to get done that day. While that may seem like a legitimate excuse for not sending thank-you messages promptly, it's not.

> **Don't be so busy in your practice that you and your team fail to properly thank people for their referrals.**

Being "busy" may be the catch-all phrase for everything people can't or don't get around to today, but it's a term that is used far too often. People use the "I'm so busy" response to everything they don't do. I'm busy, too; but I will tell you that I will never be too busy to thank people for their referrals. Never.

We have become a society that overuses the excuse of being too busy. What it really comes down to is priorities. We are almost never too busy for those things that matter to us, the things we feel are worthy. This means it's time to move the thank-you messages up on the priority list. They need to be seen for the important tool that they are, rather than the burden that some find them to be.

Your priorities should always include sending prompt thank-you messages for your referrals. There are just no two ways about this. Referrals are the lifeline of your practice. You need them like you need oxygen, so it's important to continue to promptly thank people for them. This will help keep them coming to you on a regular basis.

While I was in Savannah, Georgia, I stopped into River Street Sweets to purchase some corporate gifts. They had a handwritten thank-you note in my mailbox before I even got home from the trip. I had placed a large corporate order, and they didn't have to do anything to meet my expectations besides fulfilling the promise they made to ship a certain number of gifts for a certain amount of money. But a small, handwritten thank-you card is so unexpected in today's society that it stands out in a BIG way. Once I returned home, the company was fresh in my mind again because of their good customer service. They key here was their timing. They wasted no time in getting that message to me. The fact that it beat me home actually impressed me and made me want to tell others about it.

Don't be so busy in your practice that you and your team fail to properly thank people for their referrals. The thank-you messages should be sent out immediately. There is no good reason to hold off on getting them out, and doing so may eventually lead to falling even further behind or forgetting entirely. Get in the habit of sending out your thank-you messages right away. After a while, it will become like second nature to do it immediately following getting a new referral. Your goal is to stand out in a big way, and what will help you do that is getting a personalized thank-you message to the referrer right away.

AVOID BEING A SLACKER

It's estimated that there are over 200 billion emails sent and received each day, and that number is increasing at around 3 percent per year. In other words, people are bombarded with emails. Consider how many emails you have in your inbox when you sit down to your computer. If you are like most people, you are getting more per day than you care to, and there's also a good chance that many of them are going unread. You may be immediately deleting them or leaving them for later, but later never actually arrives.

The problem I see today is that many businesses want to take the easy route to sending a referral thank-you—they join the crowd and simply shoot off an email. Chances are, this email is also a stock one, saying the same thing to each and every new patient they get. You can see what is going to happen here: the email is going to join the plethora of all of the other messages the recipient gets all day long. It won't stand out. It probably won't even be read—and if it is read, the patient will just shrug it off as a standard message that was pretty much meaningless. You might have been better off just avoiding sending anything at all, rather than making your patients aware that you send out stock responses, especially for new referrals.

The truth is that today's technology allows companies to be too complacent about sending out thank-you messages. They have made it too easy, which has removed almost all of the meaning and effectiveness.

Automated email messages and canned thank-you cards, cranked out in mass production, are not the same as a prompt and courteous personal thank-you. A phone call, personal email, or handwritten card will always go a lot further than automated emails. And this is coming from the guy who built the largest dental and orthodontic marketing automation platform in the world. I absolutely love automated emails when they are used at the right time. However, I despise them when they let the company lose the personal touch.

Never let your practice lose the personal touch that you can have with your patients and referring sources. Referrals are largely about relationships. You can't have a relationship with an automated message or email; but you can with someone who sends personalized, handwritten messages. Focus on the relationships, keep the personal touch, and you will not only stand out, but you will build bonds with people. They will appreciate that you took the time to send them such a thank-you message. And let's be honest. No matter how busy you are, it really only takes about a minute to send out a handwritten thank-you.

Keep thank-you cards on hand, immediately write up your message, and get it into the mail as soon as you learn of the referral. Nothing replaces the personal touch, especially when it comes to wanting to build a successful referral system. Consider how many times you have gotten handwritten notes and how they made you feel, versus how automated emails with stock responses made you feel. There's a big difference. And although technology has made things easier, it doesn't mean that it has always made things *better*. This is one area that the old fashioned way beats out anything technology can offer.

This doesn't even have to be something that you do on your own. You can assign this task to someone in your office. But if you do make this part of someone's job, make sure they understand the importance of it and put in the effort. If they start to slack, you may not be aware of it, but your practice will feel the ripple from it. Keep them on board with the mission. They need to know why it's so important and to understand timing. If sending out thank-you notes is going to become the job of someone in your office, at the very least have them read this chapter of the book. It's an important task, so if you delegate this, make sure you pick the right person for the project.

THE FIRST THANK-YOU IS JUST THAT...THE FIRST

A mistake a lot of practices make is that if they do send a thank-you message, they tend to send it and then they're done. The person doesn't really ever hear from them again. While it's nice that a gesture was made in the first place, it shouldn't be the *only* thing the person hears from your office.

The first thank-you is just that—it is the *first* thank-you in a string of thank-you messages. Don't let your first thank-you end up being your only thank-you for a referral. If a patient sends you a new family, be sure to thank them promptly and then be sure to thank them again when the braces go on, when the braces come off, on the anniversary of the referral, and pretty much as often as you can.

Chances are you haven't thought of thanking the person beyond the initial contact, because that's what most people do. But just imagine how your referring source will feel when you thank them numerous times. They will know that you

> *Chances are you haven't thought of thanking the person beyond the initial contact. . .you want to get creative and keep the appreciation going.*

are thinking of them and see just how much you appreciate the referral. People love a personal touch, and they love to be remembered. They also love to get credit where credit is due. This is about making them feel special, noticed, and appreciated. Remember it's because of their trusted and generous referral that you see that patient in your practice.

Once you send the initial handwritten thank-you message, you want to get creative and keep the appreciation going. Other routes you should be taking is to list out your top referrers in your monthly newsletter, acknowledge them at your patient appreciation events with awards and prizes, and hold special VIP dinners and patient board of directors' dinners for your top referrers. All of these things are additional ways to thank your best patients.

If I told you that sending a small gift or presenting a small plaque or award at your annual patient appreciation event would be worth tens of thousands of dollars to you, how often would you do it? I'm here to tell you that all those things have the potential to do just that. When a new patient is referred to you, they are potentially worth tens of thousands of dollars. The cost of giving numerous thank-you messages in various ways is minimal compared to what comes back to you in return for those efforts.

The return on investment is always going to be worth it when it comes to putting forth the effort to thank your referral sources. Not only are you expressing gratitude, which will in turn bring you more good things, but you are also making a referral source feel so special that they will want to tell everyone they know about your office. That's priceless in terms of how it can help grow your business and increase your standing as an authority and expert in your field.

When you get a new referral, make it part of your plan to thank the referral source in multiple ways. Make sure that your office staff is on board with this, because they may see opportunities to thank sources as well. If everyone is looking for ways they can thank the referral sources, there will be a lot of gratitude and acknowledgement coming out of your office. This will go a long way toward helping your office get even more referrals.

STOP GOING AFTER ONE REFERRAL

There are far too many doctors who waste too much time trying to get one referral from everywhere. That can be exhausting and could be why so many people give up on their referral efforts. If that's what you have been doing, it's no wonder your referral system is not working well and you feel you are spending more time spinning your wheels than reaping the rewards. There's a better way to do this. Trust me.

If you haven't noticed already, there are some patients who refer over and over again. That's where you want to place your focus. We have a patient at my office who has referred seventeen patients who have successfully started treatment. Seventeen new patients from one referral source is awesome. Do you think that she gets VIP treatment in our office? You bet she does.

Find your top referrals and ask them over and over and over again. Give them more reasons to refer people to your office. If they own a business with one hundred employees, consider talking with the head of human resources to see if you can do a health fair or presentation with a special report and savings certificate for flex spending accounts. You won't get the opportunity to do this type of thing unless you ask, so don't hesitate in throwing the question out there. We have several medium-sized companies where the owner is a patient of ours, and we've infiltrated their company.

If you don't know who the top referral sources are for your practice, you are missing out.

As a result, we treat the majority of the employees and their families. We only got into that position by asking.

Avoid looking at referral sources as a one-time deal. If someone refers someone to your office, they should be considered a potential source for additional referrals going forward. After all, you already know they value your service and reputation, so why not tap into that well and see if they are able to bring in more referrals as a result?

Every time someone is referred to your office and you don't ask that referring source for more referrals, you are choosing to leave money on the table. You are overlooking an incredible source for growing your business. Rather than overlook this opportunity, focus on what you can do to encourage them to give you more referrals.

It's important to identify who your top referral sources are. This is something I have consistently told people, and it bears repeating. If you don't know who the top referral sources are for your practice, you are missing out. You are overlooking the ability to explore that list to see if you can get even more referrals from them. In my experience, those are your best routes to gaining additional new referrals. They have already shown they are willing to send people your way, and that's worth a heck of a lot. So create your list of top referring sources and guard it. That list is valuable to your practice and can help it grow.

That being said, don't rely on accidental referrals, where you get someone referred to you, but it wasn't intentional. You want the people who are doing the referring to believe in your services and knowingly send people to your office. Those are the people who will consistently send new patients to you, whereas those who accidentally send someone will probably refer no one else. After all, they never intended to send someone your way in the first place. It just so happens that they did, but they may not even be aware of it.

When you send them the initial thank-you message, however, you may discover that it actually encourages them to send you more referrals—but on purpose this time. While you don't want to set out to create accidental referrals, you want to appreciate them all the same.

So make sure you know who your top referral sources are, and treat them as the VIPs that they are.

THE 80/20 PRINCIPLE

There is a theory that I've come across many times over the years; and the more I work with other doctors in my consulting, the more I see how true this principle can be. The idea is that 80 percent of your business is coming from 20 percent of your patients. Think about that for a moment. If the 80/20 principle holds true for your office, then around 20 percent of your patients are sending you the vast majority of your business.

This is actually good news for you, because it supports my suggestion that you should create a list of your top referring sources and then treat those people like VIPs. Those are your 20 percent who are sending you numerous new patients over the years. When you can identify them and go out of your way to treat them special, you will continue to grow your business and keep a steady stream of new referrals coming in through the door.

But just because you have narrowed down who your top 20 percent are, that doesn't mean you will stop offering good service to the other 80 percent. Continue to provide the same great service you always have to *everyone* who comes to your office. But when it comes to those in the top 20 percent, go out of your way to be extra special to them. Go above and beyond, look for ways to thank them, and invite them to participate in VIP events.

There's one more thing to think about when it comes to the timing of asking for referrals or letting your patients know you appreciate them: consider doing it when they have complimented your work. When one of your patients says they love your office, they talk about how happy they are with your service, or they give you and your office any kind of positive feedback, that's a great time to thank them and ask them to please share that with their friends and family. You would be surprised at just how many will actually go on to do that. They may not have thought about referring you before; but once you ask them to, you have planted a seed that will be with them and prompt them to share your info with others more often.

When it comes to having an effective referral system for your practice, there is no *one* thing that is going to get the job done. There are many aspects to it, with some of them being as small as saying thank you and verbally letting someone know you would appreciate them telling others how much they love your office. Other gestures will be much larger, such as having VIP events. All these things together make up a great referral system. Small gestures and big ones alike plant seeds that will likely lead to the person referring you later on.

Make sure you mix up your strategy with both the little gestures and the big ones so you can cover all your bases and make an even greater impact. All those efforts together will create a great referral response. Look for ways to do the unexpected for your top 20 percent because the time put into doing so will benefit your practice far more than engaging in advertising.

WHAT DO CONSUMERS TRUST?

While you are embarking on setting up a highly effective referral system for your practice, it's important to know what the research shows about what consumers trust. In 2014, the Nielsen Company conducted research titled "Under the Influence: Consumer Trust in Advertising."

In their report, they discuss the importance of earning consumer trust and that today's consumers around the world tend to be more trusting, as compared to several years ago. The key finding in their report, however, is that word-of-mouth recommendations (referrals) are still the most influential. In fact, 84 percent of those responding stated that referrals from those they know are the most trustworthy.

The impact of referrals is on the rise, too. When Nielsen last conducted the poll, the percentage of people who felt word-of-mouth referrals was most trustworthy was around 78 percent. When you compare these referrals with the next most trusted form of advertising, word-of-mouth has quite a lead over branded websites at 69 percent, online posted reviews at 68 percent and editorials in newspapers at 67 percent.

When you compare this to where your money may be going, it's important to note that their study shows that only 60 percent trust ads in magazines, 57 percent trust ads on the radio, 55

When one of your patients gives you and your office any kind of positive feedback, that's a great time to thank them and ask them to please share that with their friends and family.

percent trust ads on television, and 42 percent trust banner ads on the Internet (although the trust for online advertising is growing). If this shows one thing definitively, it is that on average, half of the people don't trust advertising, yet businesses are spending an enormous amount of money on it each year.

This information is important to consider for several reasons. First of all, many doctors put their time and effort into advertising in newspapers and magazines, which the research shows not a lot of people trust. The research shows that the better route to take is to put effort into increasing word-of-mouth referrals, often called earned advertising. People trust it far more, and they are more apt to do business with a business that they trust.

SHARE YOUR TARGET MARKET

Oftentimes, your patients don't know what type of person they should be referring to you. This is why it's important to let them know. Give people an idea of the typical patient you are seeking. Not only do they need to know you are looking for referrals and greatly appreciate them, but they also need direction in knowing what type of person is your ideal patient.

Look for ways to start conversations about referrals so you can slip in the information about what type of patients fit your office and let people know you are seeking referrals. You can do this when they offer positive feedback, when you comment to them about how well their own treatment is progressing, or when they seem enthusiastic about their treatment.

Most people want to help you out, particularly if they like your services, but they don't always think about providing referrals. Let them know you are seeking other patients just like them. People need to be reminded that you are looking for referrals and what type of referrals you are seeking. You may have to create conversation opportunities that bring up referrals, but there's nothing wrong with that. It won't be—and shouldn't be—the only thing you are talking to them about, but it's a good idea to steer the conversation that way where you are able to without going overboard.

If you make it a priority to treat those who refer people to you extra special, you will get a lot of love in return. And by love, I mean additional referrals. You should be showering your top referring sources with gratitude and gifts. You should be holding a party every year for them, giving you the perfect opportunity to mingle with them outside of the office and making them feel special for the night.

> *Look for ways to start conversations about referrals so you can slip in the information about what type of patients fit your office and let people know you are seeking referrals.*

If you have a good relationship with some of your referral sources—and you should—then you should surprise them here and there by doing something a little crazy. Do something that really shocks them and gets them going. There is no way you can surprise them and not have them start talking about it and your office. You are pretty much forcing them to let others know about you, which is a good thing. Look for opportunities to do something for your top referring sources that will be completely unexpected. That's when you will get their attention, and they *will* talk about it to others.

Your top referrers need to know that you appreciate them, you acknowledge their efforts, and they are special to your practice. When they feel like this, they will continue to be your best source of bringing in new patients.

Don't worry about the expense that this may take; you will actually be *saving* money because you won't be doing all of that expensive advertising. Let these people speak for you rather than advertising and speaking for yourself. Remember, the people listening are going to trust them far more than they will trust your advertisement.

EMPOWERING EMPLOYEES

You can't be in all places at once, and there's no doubt that you also have your plate full of things you need to do each day and throughout the week. But you will have to make having an effective referral system a priority that cannot be overlooked in favor all of these other things. Getting your referral system in place should be at the top of your priority list. Once it is in place and you have a plan of what you will be doing and when, then you can let it run and watch the beauty of the magic that it creates. A great referral system will seem like you are putting in a minimal effort and getting back a major return.

> *There's no doubt that you have your plate full of things you need to do each day and throughout the week, but getting your referral system in place should be at the top of your priority list.*

One thing you should do is hold a meeting with your employees about this issue. You want to empower your team to treat your top 20 percent extra special. Explain to them about the importance of having a successful referral system in place and how these top people contribute to that system. Empower them so they, too, can go above and beyond for these people. They should have access to tools and goodies to help you reach out to your VIP list. Your employees be able to keep a stack of gift cards handy they can send out, or to include referrer thank-you messages in your monthly newsletter, or to send a box of locally-made cookies to one of your VIPs.

Your team should be made up of people you trust, who you feel will best carry out your mission. They also need to be on board with your goals and help you get there. If they know the importance of helping you with the referral system, they will also take pride in reaching out to the VIPs. There may be times when your office staff has more contact with these important people than you do, so give them the opportunity and ability to connect with them and make them feel special on your behalf.

When your top referring sources feel love and appreciation from not only you, but your whole office, you will have a patient for life. You will also have someone who is going to continuously promote your office to others. This is a chance to grow your practice that you don't want to let slip by. When people visit your office for treatment, they are usually treated by a team, not just by you or one particular person. Everyone in your office needs to be on the same page when it comes to the importance of referrals. They need to treat your top VIPs like the gold that they are.

If you look around your office and you don't feel your team is capable of providing this level of service, then perhaps it is time to make some changes. Don't let some members of your team hold you back and negate your efforts. Get them on board with the proper training if that is what they need, but be sure you have people in your office with the right attitude for providing excellent customer service and for going out of their way to treat VIPs as extra special. Everyone in your office is an extension of you and your practice. It's crucial that the attitude and actions they are engaging in are ones you want associated with your practice and that they help further your mission, not hold it back.

CHAPTER NINE

HOW TO USE THE REFERRAL SYSTEM TO PUT YOUR INTERNAL MARKETING ON AUTOPILOT

EVERYTHING IN BUSINESS HAS A LIFE CYCLE, AND THE REFERRAL PROCESS IS NOT IMMUNE TO this. There's a life cycle taking place, even if you haven't been purposely trying to apply yourself to participating in it. The problem is that if you haven't been aware of this cycle, there is a good chance it's not working in your favor. You can do more to ensure that you have a referral life cycle that keeps working in your favor and bringing in more and more referrals.

THE IDEAL LIFE CYCLE

Take a moment to think about what your most ideal situation ever would be. What would the perfect referral life cycle look like to you? What would happen from beginning to end with each and every referral you get? Don't worry about something seeming outlandish or over the top. Really give it some thought and see what you can do with it. Think through your perfect referral life cycle and ask yourself this: "What would be the most ideal situation to occur after someone refers that would encourage more referrals?"

Think about all the possibilities and brainstorm some ideas you feel would be ideal in following up and reaching out to your referral sources. Do you want a handwritten thank-you note to go out in the mail within seven days? What about a follow-up thank-you phone call and personalized email on or about the same day the letter hits the patient's mailbox? You could make sure that every referral gets a small birthday cake on their birthday, a small treat at each holiday, and a cool surprise for the holidays. Whatever your best scenario looks like, write it down.

Once you visualize your most ideal situation ever, it's time to automate the entire process. You can do this a lot easier than you may realize by using a software program such as InfusionSoft. This program will remind your team who needs a handwritten thank-you card today, queue up the phone calls and emails, and ship gifts and letters with your own personalized handwriting. This makes it simple for you to automate your entire ideal situation and be able to do this for your top VIP list.

By making effective use of contact management software, you will be able to keep all of your VIPs organized, automate everything that you need to remember, integrate it with other systems, run reports that can give you helpful insight, and much more. Most people don't realize just how important using a system like this is until they finally give it a try. The only question they have is why they didn't start using it sooner.

TAPPING OTHERS

Any time you can get the chance to pick someone's brain who is good at sales and marketing, you should do it. You would be surprised at the things you can pick up by asking these people some questions. Even if out you learn only one new little tidbit of useful information, it will still be worth your time. Every good nugget of info you get is going to add up; and if you put them to use, they can help to grow your practice.

While I was visiting Disney World once, I purposely sat through their timeshare sales presentation. I know most people would roll their eyes or take off running in the other direction at the thought of something like this. But I wanted to sit through it so I could see if there was anything I could learn from watching them in action and asking questions afterward.

I've never been shy, so I had no problem peppering the sales team with my questions. I asked them how long they continue to follow up with one of their leads, what they do after someone does decide to buy, etc. They don't often spill the beans when people are asking about their process, but they will divulge some great secrets if you push hard enough. Here's one of them: Disney Vacation Club has a sixty-month sequence—an astounding five years of follow-up—that happens after you purchase a timeshare with them. Everything is built around the goal of encouraging you to refer a friend or family member who will also become a Disney Vacation Club member.

This information got me thinking about what others do. How many small businesses will stop following up after five weeks, five days, or five minutes of encouraging a new customer to refer friends and family? Not many people will stick with it for a period of five years. That's just amazing, and it's no wonder that the Disney Vacation Club is so successful. Others can learn a lot from the success of the Disney company in terms of what they do to go above and beyond in providing customer service, but also in what they are doing to stick with a customer to try to get referrals from them.

Many of us would not even consider trying to get a referral from someone for a period of five years, but Disney doesn't seem to bat an eye at it. They obviously know something that we don't. There must be people who are making the referral years after their initial purchase. They have tried it, tracked it, and see that it is well worth their time to continue to reach out to people into the fifth year after their purchase.

How long do you think it's worth reaching out to people after their initial visit or completing treatment? If you are like most other doctors, you are not doing it nearly long enough. If you give up on your efforts a month or six months into it, imagine what you could potentially be walking away from.

What is the cost of putting in the effort for a longer period of time? Chances are, it's well worth it.

> There's no doubt that you have your plate full of things you need to do each day and throughout the week, but getting your referral system in place should be at the top of your priority list.

We live in a world today where everyone wants instant gratification. The same goes for wanting referrals. If people don't see them immediately, they are disappointed and want to walk away. But having the patience and determination to stick with it will likely pay off in a big way. Keep stoking the fire and planting the seeds so that when the person is ready and the opportunity presents itself, *you* are the doctor they are ready to refer. They may not know someone else at that exact moment who needs braces, for example; but maybe a year down the road they will. You want to be the one they think of, and that means continuing to follow up with them so you are the one on their mind.

WHEN TO ASK FOR REFERRALS

As I previously mentioned, timing is important when it comes to asking for referrals. Do you know the best points in the relationship where you should be asking for referrals? Most doctors I've worked with think that it's when the braces come off. Sure, that's a great time to ask for referrals, but patients are actually most excited when the braces are first going *on*. They are feeling hopeful and excited about the promise of what the treatment is going to do for them. They are feeling great, and they love your office for helping them get started on this transformational journey.

When patients first get their braces on, their mouth may be a little sore; and yes, they might be adjusting to living with braces. But just because you and I may think a patient isn't excited at the beginning of treatment, the research simply doesn't support our assumptions. Surprising to most doctors is that patients are typically much more excited at the beginning of treatment than at the end.

It's important to grasp the idea that patients are just as likely to refer—and in many cases *more* likely to refer—at the beginning of treatment than at the end. If you're missing this critical time to talk about referrals, you are absolutely leaving money on the table. Don't wait until the treatment is over to ask about referrals. Make a point to ask about them when treatment is first started—but don't stop there. Keep asking during treatment and then again when they finish. Then follow up for a couple of years after they have finished treatment. Be more like the Disney Vacation Club so you are getting those referrals even if their friends and family members don't need braces until two to three years down the road.

HARNESSING THE POWER

Consumers are most excited about a product or service the minute they decide to buy. Some may have buyer's remorse in the following days, but our job is to boost that time they spend at the peak and extend the good feelings.

You can do this through a variety of ways: testimonials, video evidence of other people who love your practice, tips and support tools to help them get through the first few weeks, and ever-present reminders that your practice thrives on referrals. Think about all of the things you should be including in that system, such as contests, events, newsletter stories, patient-of-the-month features, testimonials, books, reports, and more. All of these things help serve the expectation that patients in this practice talk about us to their friends and family.

Take the reins and lead the way when it comes to setting the tone for how people will feel about your office when they walk out the door. Don't allow it to just take its own course and hope for the best. Make it part of your plan to help people feel good about making the choice to get their treatment at your office. Ensure that they will see lots of positive images about your practice from others that will reinforce their decision to have their treatment done at your office. Keep in mind that it's not advertising they need to see here; it's going to be far more beneficial for them to see information from other satisfied patients who will speak on your behalf. They will trust those messages far more than if you put some ads in front of them.

Not only will having all of these items in place and ready to go help those who have already made the decision to get their treatment at your office, but it is good for those who are still deciding, too. You will be able to use things like testimonials, patient videos, and success stories to help others who may be on the fence decide in your favor. Invest the time in creating a collection of these items that are ready to go and easily accessible in a variety of formats.

> *Like most things in life, you will get out of your referral system what you put into it. Put in a minimal effort, and you can expect minimal results.*

What you do for those who refer people to your office is completely in your hands. You can choose to be a doctor who does nothing and puts in a minimal effort, or you can be the one who makes a bold statement by showing gratitude. It's all up to you. Determine what you want to do and map out the plan to make it happen. As you consider this, think about what each level of engagement will bring you in return. You can only imagine that choosing to do nothing is not going to do much to help grow your practice. But if you do a lot, you will get a lot in return.

Like most things in life, you will get out of your referral system what you put into it. Put in a minimal effort, and you can expect minimal results. Put in an exceptional effort, and you will get exceptional results. Which one is going to help grow your business and bring you the level of success you are seeking? In this field, as with most others, you have to be intentional with what you want to do in order to get the results you want.

THE IMPORTANCE OF INTERNAL MARKETING

Entrepreneurs spend a lot of time trying to get people to notice them and do business with them. Yet most of the time, they put all of their efforts into external things. They look outward seeking new patients, putting all of their focus there. While you *do* want to put forth some of your effort externally, you don't want to forget about your internal marketing efforts and just how important they are to bringing in new patients.

Your staff holds the key to bringing in a lot of new referrals. Your employees need to feel connected to your practice and to your mission. If they don't, they can undermine everything you are doing to get referrals, and you may not even be aware of it. Employees need not only to be on board with what you are doing and have an excellent grasp of how your referral system works, but they need to be unified. They need to feel like a team that is working on your behalf to reach practice goals and bring in new patients. They need to have a shared sense of purpose.

Your job in getting your employees on board is not only to tell them about what you are doing and what your goals are with your referral system, but to sell them on the idea. They need to believe it, see the beauty of it, and be completely sold on the idea when it comes to carrying it out. They need to have a passion for your brand and in bringing in referrals. They need to hear all of the same things you are telling people externally. The goal is to bring your brand alive to them and help them make a connection, just as you do when trying to reach people externally.

Don't make the mistake of putting all of your time and energy into external resources. Take a look around your office and realize you are sitting on a potential gold mine. When you have mastered your internal marketing, you will have everything on autopilot. They will want to help you every step of the way and will have the system working flawlessly as you continue working on other things.

At its most basic level, internal marketing is getting your staff aligned with the same message your potential patients are getting. They need to know what that message is and believe in it. The goal in internal marketing is that once you get your staff on board, they will provide the best patient service imaginable.

WHY INTERNAL MARKETING

Most doctors overlook internal marketing, which is a big mistake. What they don't realize is that patients are referring you based on the office experience as a whole, not just a single person in the office. When someone refers your office, they mention your name as who to go see, but they are really talking about your entire office experience. They believe in the whole package.

Let's imagine for a moment that you are providing amazing service and the patients loved you. Yet when they try to call and set an appointment, the person on the phone is cold to them and doesn't seem very eager to fit them in for an appointment that met their scheduling needs. Is that type of person helping or hindering future referrals? Of course it's going to hinder future referrals, because the patient is going to believe that setting an appointment at your office is difficult. The same goes for working with your treatment coordinator, billing department, or anyone else in your office. The patient needs the entire process of visiting your office to be great, from the first phone call to paying the bill. If it's anything less in any particular area, they will have doubts about sending you referrals.

Patients and other referral sources refer places based on the *entire* experience. Every interaction that the person has with someone in your office is making them either want to refer you or refrain from doing so. The entire team helps to shape that patient's experience at your office.

Companies such as Apple know this is true. That's why they make every effort to provide excellent service from the very first phone call you make to them. Google probably gets this better than most other companies do, which is probably why they earn billions each year and the figure continues to have double-digit revenue growth percentages. They understand the importance of internal marketing and culture so much that they have someone who holds the job title of being Google's Jolly Good Fellow.

Chade-Meng Tan, their Jolly Good Fellow, has one job at Google—to spread happiness among the people who work there. He spends hours just trying to get people to understand the basic concepts of happiness and how to be happier. He encourages them to do a wide variety of things, such as meditating, practicing compassion, and understanding mindfulness. His efforts include holding conferences and seminars for employees and getting them involved in happiness-inducing practices as often as possible.

Why would Google spend so much time focusing internally on their team, to the extent of hiring someone whose job it is to help make the employees happy and to improve the company culture? Because they completely acknowledge that employees will make or break you. They may be internal, but they have a major influence over the experience that everyone has externally. If the people at Google are happier, they are more likely to provide better customer service. If the company culture at Google is good and people are nice to each other and like being around one another, the atmosphere will be positive and exciting.

> *Patients and other referral sources refer places based on the* **entire** *experience.*

Google knows this, and so do your patients. They can sense unhappy staff just as well as they can a team of people who love what they do and enjoy being around each other. All of this has a huge impact on the type of service your patients will receive when they deal with your office. Whether the interaction is on a phone call, during an office visit, or at an outside event, the attitude is always there reminding them about the good or bad of your office. Google wants to make sure that when their employees deal with their external customers, they are happy and are providing great service. They also realize that happy employees will be more engaged, more productive, and more enthusiastic about helping the company grow. When your employees are happy, they are also more productive, so your office will get more done without you having to lead them along and coax them through everything. They will want to take initiative and help make things great in your office.

Getting your employees in the right mindset is crucial. It's going to pay off both with the interactions they have externally, as well as with the culture and atmosphere that is experienced internally. Your staff are a reflection of your entire practice, so it is imperative they are putting forth the image you want them to. When you invest in internal marketing to get your staff in the right frame of mind, you are always going to see a great return on investment. If you don't invest—you overlook it and do nothing— your office will pay a much higher price. And that price will be the referrals you will lose out on, which would be many.

WAYS TO BOOST INTERNAL MARKETING

Knowing just how important internal marketing is for your practice is just the start. Your next move is to actually put it into *action*. There are many ways you can do this—and the first step starts with yourself. Ensure that your attitude is in the right place and invites happiness and good attitudes around you. Remember, attitudes can be catching, so make sure that yours is worth being caught. You are always setting the example for others in your office on the type of behavior and attitude that is expected. If they see you happy, enthusiastic, and eager to please patients, there is a good chance they will want to follow suit.

Once you have your own head in the game, it's time to work on your team. Hold a meeting to let everyone know that this is the new direction your office is taking. Make it a team project where everyone is going to be pulling together to ensure that customer service is the top priority. Empower your employees to make some service decisions on their own so they will have the opportunity to do what is best for the practice and will feel a part of the growing success.

While you are going to do a lot of talking at this meeting, do some listening, too. Ask your staff what kind of questions or concerns they may have, as well as for feedback on ways they feel the customer service experience can be improved. They see things you may not be aware of. They may be proposing small gestures, such as putting fresh magazines in the lobby, but all of these small efforts will add up to a better experience. This will also help your employees feel their input on how to improve a patient's experience was valued, rather than just dismissed as something small or petty.

While in the meeting, it's a good idea to brainstorm a list of every way your team comes into contact with the public. This is going to include by phone, in person, through social media, at events, etc. Consider all places where it is possible so that the plan for each of these places can be reviewed to make sure your message is consistent and that the tools and information you need available at each place is ready to go. If you identify an area that is lacking—perhaps you aren't responding to the messages received through the Facebook page—then it needs to be remedied immediately. Make it all part of the plan.

Find a way to keep the momentum from this meeting going. Oftentimes doctors will have one meeting, get people fired up, and then allow a year to go by without another one. Over the course of that year, the excitement that was built up at the meeting will tend to wane. You want to make sure that you keep the fire burning by adding another log here and there. At the start of each morning, Walmart employees gather in one area of the store for a brief meeting. They do this out in the open and customers can walk by and see it taking place. During this brief meeting, the store manager on that shift goes over a few things that need to be addressed, then says a few words of wisdom to remind people about providing great customer service. Finally, the store manager acts as a coach by getting the employees pumped up to start their shift and kick off the morning in a great way.

> *If you identify an area that is lacking, then it needs to be remedied immediately. Make it all part of the plan.*

Such quick reminders help get the team all on the same page and remind them that providing great service is a top priority. Whether you hold a five-minute mini session at the start of each day, a 10-minute meeting each week, or a 30-minute meeting each month, just be sure that you are bringing everyone back together for this type of thing. Every great coach on the planet brings their team into a huddle to help them get their head in the game and remind them of what the priority is. When you do this, you will keep your message and motive fresh in their minds, build up their enthusiasm, and maintain the good atmosphere you want your office known for.

During at these meetings, don't hesitate to point out great deeds done by your employees. While you don't want it to become a contest where they are pitted against each other, you do want to recognize great service and dedication. Throw them some verbal kudos by pointing out a job well done and surprise them here and there by bringing in lunch or handing out gift cards for Starbucks. These small gestures will keep your team fired up and ready to help you provide the best possible patient experience around.

GIVING THEM WHAT THEY NEED

In order to set your internal marketing on autopilot, you will also want to make sure your employees have access to everything they need to properly promote your office. This means you should keep enough brochures and referral gifts on hand, provide time for work-related social media updates, and more. When these things are readily available, they can streamline your entire system, making it seem nearly effortless. And you will get a big return.

Additionally, it is important to make sure that your employees receive ongoing training when and where it is needed. I know many doctors don't cover the expense of keeping up on employee training, but it is well worth the effort to do so. Your staff needs to have the training and be apprised of the latest information in the field to do their jobs effectively. When they can do their jobs effectively, they are helping to keep your patients satisfied, improving the overall experience at your office, and being more productive. It's also a good

> *Employees always need to know the expectations for their specific position, but also what is expected of them as part of a team in helping to elevate your practice as a whole.*

idea to encourage your employees to collaborate on patient experience efforts so they can realize that no matter what area of your office they work in, they are all a unified team and can assist each other. Remember, it's the overall experience people have in visiting your office that matters and will keep them referring people or not.

Your employees need to be able to relate to your practice, feel like they are a part of it, and participate in the patient experience as much as possible. This is the best route to getting them all on board with making the patient the priority. When you have mastered internal marketing, it will operate on autopilot, allowing you to reap the rewards with very little noticeable effort. Your employees will also feel empowered, responsible, and accountable for helping the practice perform well, and will provide the level of service that will bring in many referrals.

One of the reasons many employees in a doctor's office don't put in a major effort toward the patient experience is because they don't see their position as making a difference either way. They feel that they are "only" the receptionist, treatment coordinator, billing contact, etc. It's important they begin to realize that every single position in your practice collaborates and combines together to create one patient experience. Every position in your office is important, because every position affects the patient in some manner.

Employees always need to know the expectations for their specific position, but also what is expected of them as part of a team in helping to elevate your practice as a whole. Don't assume they know these things; rather, make it a priority to establish it with them and help reinforce it as time goes on. Those expectations may even change as time goes on if they are with you for a long time. Just make sure that if expectations change, you have open communication so you can share that information with them.

PUTTING IT ALL TOGETHER

In the beginning of this chapter, I asked you to take a moment to consider what your most ideal situation ever would be when it came to addressing each referral, from beginning to end. That information you came up with is an important part of what is going to put your internal marketing on autopilot. There is a good chance that most of your *A successful referral system starts on the inside and works its way to the outside.* ideas in the beginning of this chapter revolved only around what that ideal situation would be for the referral or referring source; you were not focused on the staff in your office at all. That's what internal marketing is all about.

You absolutely do have to consider all factors that affect your office externally, but don't make the mistake of overlooking your internal marketing. Your employees are a huge part of your practice and the overall patient experience. When you turn some of your focus on them, you will find they will in turn help make your external marketing efforts go a lot smoother. It's well worth the effort to determine your most ideal office staff ever and the best possible way they could treat your patients and represent your business—and then put that into action.

When it comes to having a stellar referral system that will continually keep your practice busy and growing, there are numerous factors to consider. Internal marketing is a great piece of that puzzle; and when you can master that, you will begin to set the system on autopilot. A successful referral system starts on the inside and works its way to the outside. Work on getting everything situated on the inside first, from your employees to your referral life cycle. Once you have everything right on the inside of your practice, it can't help but to help push that success to the outside world, too.

CHAPTER TEN
KEY METRICS AND PERFORMANCE INDICATORS FOR RAPID PRACTICE SUCCESS

As with many aspects of business, unless you are tracking and measuring what you are doing, it's difficult to know if you are making any progress. When the numbers are up in the air and people have no clue what they are, it's difficult to say they want to get from point A to point B. They haven't established what point A is, so there's no way to know how to get to point B or what it would even take to get there. I see this frequently in my consulting; and I know it is an area that holds doctors back, especially when it comes to their referral system.

What I find most often is that there are many practices that *do* track referrals per month, or even referrals per new patient. Yet there are very few practices that are tracking the lifetime customer value of those referrals by source. This concept will take you a step further, so you are going beyond just knowing the monthly or yearly referral statistic; you will be able to actually *use* this information to help grow your business.

DIVERSIFYING REFERRALS

We all want referrals, and we are happy to get all the referrals we can, regardless of where they are coming from or why someone may have referred the person to us. But what you may not have considered before is whether or not your referrals are diversified. When you think about where and why you get all of your referrals, do they all come from the same place and for the same reason? This can be disastrous if conditions change, so it is imperative that your practice diversify when it comes to getting referrals.

115

Dental referrals and dental hygiene referrals are great, but what if the offices referring to you only refer your office because you take the same type of insurance program? What happens if you decide to stop taking that insurance program? What if all of your referrals are coming from one particular dentist's office and that dentist decides to retire? I've seen issues like this completely devastate a specialty practice when they haven't taken the time and initiative to diversify their referral sources.

Think about how Apple does business for just a moment. The company squeezes its vendors to deliver their components (such as glass screens for an iPhone) quicker and cheaper than any other company on the planet. Often, they require the companies to set up next door to Apple's facilities in China so that there are no delays in shipping or raw materials fulfillment. It's great for Apple, but very scary for the third-party vendors who are over-reliant on one big company for their business. What would happen to these third-party vendors if Apple sales suddenly plummeted or Apple decided to use another vendor? There is a good chance they would crumble, because all of their business is coming from one account.

> *One of the best ways to get more referrals is to start **giving** more referrals.*

You should try to position yourself as Apple does where everyone around you relies on your success. You can do this by having successful and massive referral systems and marketing programs that generate more new patients that you can refer out to general dentists when the patient finds you first and needs a referral to a general dentist. When you refer more people back out to the general dentist than they refer to your office, you have placed yourself in the toll booth position of being the owner of a massive list of patients and a valuable resource to help your referring dentists through their association with you.

One of the best ways to get more referrals is to start *giving* more referrals. When you refer people, they will automatically start reciprocating that favor to you. Examine who you are sending referrals to and what improvements you can make in this area. Let people know that you are going to be increasing the number of referrals you are sending to them. This will put it on their radar; and they will begin thinking of you when they need to refer patients, too.

When you diversify your referrals, you will not have to worry as much about something happening to your primary source and the stream of new patients drying up. You will have referrals coming into your office from a variety of sources, giving your office a layer of security and strength that would be difficult to have without that diversification. It's wonderful to have top referral sources and to treat them like the VIPs that they are, but you never want all of your referrals all coming from the same one or two places. That's a risk that should be avoided. Not only can it cost you if the dynamics of the relationship happen to change, but it could be costing you in the long run if you could be bringing in higher quality patients from other sources.

WHY MEASURE

Peter Drucker said that if you can't measure it, you can't manage it. We can all take a lesson from this piece of advice and use it to make our practices more successful. Most doctors give lip service about wanting more referrals, acknowledge the importance of referrals, and even say they are taking action to encourage more referrals. But when I ask them how many referrals they had last month, the majority have no idea. Not only do most not measure the referrals, but they are not even aware they are not doing it. Many doctors think they are putting in far greater effort in this area than they really are.

To truly manage your referrals and referral system, you have to keep track of it. You need to know the numbers and information. Only when you know where the referrals are coming from, why you are getting them, and how many are coming your way each week will you be able to use that information to better grow your referral rate and business.

If you do not measure or track your referral sources, you will have no control over the system. Without having any control over your referral system, you can't expect it to be successful or to bring in the people you both want and need in order to sustain your practice and help it grow. Sure, you could likely survive by just taking what referrals you get and hoping that some people also just so happen to choose you without having someone refer them to your office. But why would you want to continue down such a path? You can do better than that. In fact, you can create a system that will bring you a steady supply of new patients and help you create the practice that you envision. You can't improve the system you have in place until you measure to know where you are. Once you know that, you will be able to make changes that will help take you where you want to be.

"If you can't measure it, you can't manage it."

~Peter Drucker

If you have already been keeping track (at least minimally) of the referrals you get each month, you will have a starting point to build off of. If you haven't, then you will have to come up with a number by taking a ballpark guess at how many referrals you get in a typical month. Start out by setting a goal for your referrals based on historical data. This is going to be the best and most accurate way to determine where you are and what you can safely expect to gain each month, without even upping your game.

Wherever you are with the number of referrals you have been getting each month, you want to build on that amount. If you have only averaged twenty referrals per month over the last six to twelve months, try setting a goal with your team to get to twenty-five referrals per month. Discuss this goal with your employees and get them on board with the effort to increase the monthly referrals. Listen to their ideas on how they think you may be able to encourage referrals. There are plenty of ways you can do this, and you shouldn't be hesitant to try various strategies to determine which ones work best for you.

Take a look at some of the ways you have been getting referrals thus far. What tactics have you used up to this point? Brainstorm a list of possible ways you can get new referrals, starting with what you have been doing so far. Here are some additional ideas to consider:

- **Hold in-office contests where you give prizes based on new referrals in a given period of time.** You can give small gift cards or possibly award a bigger prize through a random drawing once each quarter. For the yearly prize, think about something like a weekend getaway with all expenses paid. This will provide a great incentive for people to want to make referrals to your office. In-office contests should be done regularly throughout the year. Instead of keeping the contest going all year long, you can make them short contests so there is excitement and a sense of urgency. If you have one quarterly, for example, that will motivate people to get busy sending referrals, and then there can be one overall yearly contest using the data collected from the quarterly efforts.

- **Hold time-bound incentive deals for referrals.** People often act quickly if they know that the window of opportunity is closing. Hold a short contest that gives people one or two weeks only to get in as many referrals as they can. They will quickly get to work making those connections so they can have a chance at winning the prize. Anytime you can create a sense of urgency, where there is a deadline people need to beat, they will be more likely to take action. When there is no time-bound incentive, they can put it off and procrastinate for a long time—even forever in some cases.

- **Surprise some of your patients.** If you know someone is sick at home, send them a get-well care package. If you know it's someone's birthday, send them a card from the office, along with a gift card for lunch. If you have a teen who is going to be performing in a recital, have a bouquet of flowers delivered wishing them luck on behalf of your practice. When you surprise your patients, you will get them talking. And when they talk and say good things, they are automatically referring people to your office. As I always say, nobody talks about things that are boring. If you do something that surprises people, that is out of the ordinary and anything but boring, people will talk. When they talk, they are referring your office, whether they are doing so intentionally or not. Just by talking positively about your practice, they are sending messages that people will remember later. The person hearing it may not even remember where they heard the positive stories from, but they often remember that they heard good things about your practice, making them more likely to call for an appointment and to refer you to someone else they know who may be looking for a doctor.
- **Patient appreciation events are a great way to build relationships.** As I discussed previously, you should be regularly hosting patient appreciation events. These are low-cost opportunities that allow people to see you in a relaxed environment where they can talk to you. People refer doctors whom they trust and feel they know. It's all based on relationships. It's difficult to build strong ties with people if you only see them when they are in the chair for treatment. You need opportunities to see them outside the office where you can chat and let them see you having some fun.
- **Send invitations to VIPs for an open house where you can treat them special—providing prizes, food, and more.** Really go out of your way to make them feel important so they share the excitement of this event with others. The people you invite to this event will be those already at the top of your referral list.
- **Get your office engaged in doing some community service work.** People love to see doctors giving back to those in need in their community. It will help people realize you care about others and want to help. Then they will be more inclined to send people your way. For example, you can offer some pro bono services to those who don't

have the money or insurance to start treatment. Another option is to find a group you can get involved with, even if it's to sponsor a 5K race they may be having. Each person who sees your involvement is an opportunity to spread the good word of your efforts in giving back. You can also get people in your office on board with this as well. Make it a team effort where they will be representing your practice.

- **Offer family member incentives and discounts to start treatment.** This is an ideal way to recruit new people, because everyone loves being able to get a special deal. Let people know this is an exclusive discount only available to those who are family members of people already getting treatment. Creating that air of exclusivity will motivate people to refer you to their family members.

Referrals, as I've touted before and will always remind people of, are the best possible form of advertising that your practice can engage in. There's no pressure for anyone to sell anything; and with the pressure gone, there are only relaxed and trusted referrals taking place. Whether you are doing a variety of the tactics above, engaging in social media photo contests, or using newsletter inserts, there are plenty of ways to reach people and increase your referrals. In fact, there are ideas to help you do it all around you. It's just a matter of changing your mindset to identify the opportunities to get referrals and start acting on them.

DETERMINING YOUR REFERRAL RATE

To determine your referral rate, you will need to know where each new patient is coming from. Getting this information should be standard practice because it's important to know. Find out if they were a referral from another patient or a dentist's office, or maybe they responded to one of your marketing pieces or articles. Whatever it is, you need to know so you can determine what is working as well as what the lifetime value of a referral is. Only when you have tracked where your referrals are coming from—and have done so in a meticulous manner—will you know the truth about your referrals. Give it a try, because you may be surprised at what you find out. I've worked with many doctors who had no idea where their referrals were coming from, or they thought they were coming from one place only to discover they were actually coming from another. The information can be eye-opening and change how you handle your whole referral system. Take the time to find out where your referrals come from so you can tap into those sources and create a river of steady new business for your office.

LEVERAGING SOURCES

While you may not have considered it before, there is a good chance that *where* your referrals originate from is also going to make a difference. Some are going to turn out to be more valuable than others; and if you can establish a pattern of that taking place, you will be able to leverage those sources of lucrative referrals to increase your bottom line. If you only have one or two places where all of your referrals are originating, then you are leaving money on the table because there are others out there—and possibly some sources that will bring you more referrals of higher value.

At this point, you should track long-term customer value, such as collections, referrals, additional products and services purchased, etc.—all by referral source. Determine what each type of referral activity you are engaging in is bringing you so you can determine where your efforts are paying off— or where they are better spent. You might think your referral appreciation programs are too expensive until you do the math and discover that patients who are referred throughout your annual movie night are three times more likely to refer someone else, and eight times more likely to pay in full compared to someone referred by a dentist or insurance company.

Knowing this type of information is crucial when it comes to upping your game in bringing in more quality referrals. I don't know your math, but I do know that *you* must know your math. You can only make wise investments in further marketing and leveraging the programs that work in your practice if you approach them with facts. In order to have those facts, you have to do the leg work to evaluate every effort you are making when it comes to getting referrals. Obtaining these data might seem like a time-consuming task, and at first it is. But it will save you a lot of time in the long run because you will no longer be

> If you only have one or two places where all of your referrals are originating, then you are leaving money on the table because there are others out there—and possibly some sources that will bring you more referrals of higher value.

spending time and money on activities you know will not bring in the type of referrals you are seeking. It will help you cut to the chase and implement only the types of programs that will bring in top-of-the-line referrals for your office.

You have to determine which referral sources are converting and bringing in quality people who start treatment. What you don't know about your referral sources is absolutely hurting your business, so make it a priority to analyze the data and determine as much information about your referral sources as possible.

As you are learning, having a successful referral system is much more than just asking people to refer their friends and family. More thought goes into it, evaluations take place behind the scenes, and decisions are made for going forward. Each of these steps is used to strengthen the referral system until it becomes second nature, works like a well-oiled machine, and brings in a steady stream of referrals that will grow your office. It is something I have done and helped many other doctors do. And it's something you can do, too.

SUCCESSFUL REFERRALS

Have you ever thought about what a successful referral is? If someone calls your office for information, is that a successful referral? Or is it when someone begins treatment? Or finishes treatment? Answering these questions will help you be able to measure and analyze. If you have a successful referral, it's safe to say they are someone who had some type of treatment performed by your office.

There are varying levels of degrees of successful referrals, too. While someone may be a successful referral who both begins and finishes treatment, an even more successful referral will be one that does this and also refers others to you along the way. Make sure you can clearly define what a successful referral is for your own practice. You will need to keep this in mind when setting goals you want to strive for, as well as when you hold referral contests. The last thing you want is someone claiming they won the contest because a referral was just a phone call of inquiry or a free consultation appointment.

Ideally, a successful referral should be someone who has started treatment at your office. Once treatment has begun, you can confidently consider that person to be a successful referral. Up until that point, there are no guarantees they will ever start treatment or convert to actually being a patient. Waiting for the treatment to be completed before considering the person to be a successful referral can be problematic because it makes people wait too long for contest results; and sometimes people may switch offices to finish their treatment for reasons that have nothing to do with you, such as moving out of the area.

THE THREE TYPES OF REFERRALS

There are different types of referrals some like to refer to as A-list, B-list, and C-list referrals. The A-list referrals are those people who are immediately ready to begin treatment. They call your office knowing what they want to get started with and they easily commit to beginning treatment at your office. These are the best kind of referrals your office can have, because very little time is spent working on getting them started with treatment. They come to you ready to go.

The B-list referrals are also good, but they don't come to you completely ready to get started like the A-list ones do. This list of referrals will take a little bit of work on your part to get them committed to starting treatment.

The C-list referrals are those who likely need the treatment, but they are trying to avoid it or put it off as long as they can. They know that it's probably inevitable they will get the treatment, but they have reservations about doing so. The C-list referrals are going to be your least desirable because they will eat up too much time and energy in trying to get them to convert.

You will be ahead of the game if you can begin to identify your referrals as falling into one of these three categories. If you do, you can save yourself some time. Focus on the A-list first, as they are going to convert quickly and will likely send you more A-list referrals as they go along. Next, give your attention to the B-list referrals that you'll have to spend a little bit of time to get them converted and starting treatment. Finally, when it comes to your C-list of referrals, give them very little of your time and attention. They may never start treatment despite your best efforts to persuade them to do so, and they will likely only give you C-list referrals, if any at all.

PATIENT RETENTION

While we are focused on getting new referrals, it is important to touch upon the importance of maintaining your current patients, too. Experts find that it often costs a company six to seven times more money to acquire a new customer than it does to retain their current ones. If you are doing things to lose patients, causing them to transfer their treatment to another doctor in your area, you are costing yourself a lot of time and money. Not only are those people not finishing out their treatment—which is costing you—but they are also telling others why they are not going back to your office to complete their treatment. That alone is also going to cost you future referrals.

The best way to avoid this problem is to consistently make your patients top priority and give them the best possible care around. When you do this, they will have little reason to transfer their treatment elsewhere. Pay attention to how your patients feel and to the feedback they give regarding your care. And not just yours, but that of your entire office as well. Listen to them and ask questions so you can find out if they are happy. If there is a sign of any type of problem, fix it before it grows, or at least address the issue to the best of your ability once it surfaces.

Gaining a lot of new referrals is not going to do much to help your practice if you repeatedly lose patients due to poor treatment in your office or an overall unsatisfactory patient experience. If you see patients making the switch to another office, and the switch isn't the result of their moving out of the area, come right out and ask them to be honest about what the problem is. You can only fix the problems that may drive patients elsewhere if you are aware of them.

Your churn rate refers to the patients who have started getting treatment at your office and then have stopped. Perhaps those people have stopped getting treatment altogether, but what's more likely is they have switched to a new office. Most people who begin treatment tend to see it through to the end, whether that is going to be at your office or not. If you have a high churn rate, it's important to find out why. There has to a reason why your patients are not being loyal to your office and are finishing their treatment elsewhere. If you don't know what it is right off the top of your head, find out what is driving them away. Let them know you care and want to know why.

> *Pay attention to how your patients feel and to the feedback they give regarding your care, and that of your entire office as well.*

You want to have a low churn rate. If someone comes into your office and makes the decision to begin treatment, then almost always, barring special circumstances, they should also *finish* treatment with your office. If they are not, you should be concerned and the problem should be identified so it can be rectified. For every person who begins treatment with your office and leaves to finish somewhere else, your office is losing money and referrals.

When you think about your patients, consider the ones who are currently undergoing treatment but don't forget about those who have completed treatment, too. Everyone who has completed treatment with your office is also a potential source for sending you referrals. Continue to reach out to those people, rather than giving up and assuming they are done with their treatment and will no longer need your services. Things change over time. And you never know if they will need treatment for something else, if they go on to get married and have children and grandchildren, or if they come across friends who need a good practice such as yours.

BENEFITS OF REFERRALS

Now is probably a good time to remind you of the many benefits of referrals. This is what it's all about and why we are working so hard to create a successful referral system. For starters, referrals are people who are going to be a lot easier to get to come in for appointments, as well as to convert into patients who begin treatment. They are calling your office because someone they know trusted you, and that counts for a whole lot in the consumer world. Nobody wants a poor experience, so they seek out trusted referrals from those they know and whose opinions they trust. The mere fact you were named as a referral has given you an endorsement that will help them trust you and be ready to move forward with appointments and begin treatment.

Another perk when it comes to getting referrals is that they are less likely to be focused on price. These are people more concerned with getting quality treatment and working with a doctor they can trust. They are not walking into your office looking for a basement bargain price on whatever treatment it is they may need. They want to know they can obtain the treatment from a quality doctor and that they will be happy with the results of that treatment.

People tend to like things that are consistent, so referrals are also going to be more loyal as a result. They have been referred to you by someone who trusts you so they will be consistent in trusting you most of the time, and then they will go on to continue this pattern by referring others to you as well. People also want to believe they made the right decision when they choose a doctor to begin treatment with. They will work to remain loyal to your office, so they can feel comfortable with the decision they made. In other words, you will have loyal patients from the start; and you would have to do a lot to lose that loyalty.

Having a successful referral system in place will keep people calling your office, which will free up your time to do other things. You won't have to spend your days hunting down new patients. Rather, the people on the street who have experience with you will be out there doing the work for you. During that time, you can do other things, such as take care of more patients, write books to establish yourself as an authority the field, or take that time to do any number of other things. But the time won't have to be spent trying to get people to call your office and set their first appointment.

There are many benefits to having referrals. If you haven't had a good referral system yet, you will be delighted at what it does for you once you have one in place. At the end of the day, you need people to call your office for an appointment who are ready to say yes to treatment. They are ready to get started and already know some of what is involved. That's exactly what referrals do for you. They are people who are ready to get started and make your job a whole lot easier.

WHY MOST DOCTORS DON'T ADEQUATELY THINK THROUGH THEIR REFERRAL SYSTEM AND WHAT YOU CAN DO ABOUT IT

PRIOR TO PICKING UP THIS BOOK, THERE IS A GOOD CHANCE YOU HADN'T THOUGHT MUCH about your referral system. It may have lingered in the back of your mind, or perhaps you never gave it any thought at all. Many doctors I have worked with know they should create a successful referral system, but it's always put on the back burner. It's a project that will be done someday, but that someday rarely comes for many of them.

By reading this book, you have made the first major step toward making improvements to your referral system—or toward creating one if you currently have nothing in place. There's a good chance you share the same reasons as other doctors for why you haven't focused on this issue much before, but I'm going to explain why you should start now.

UNDERSTANDING BENEFITS

In prior chapters, we have touched on some of the advantages of getting referrals versus other ways of bringing in new patients. The most common reason I have found that doctors do not have a referral system in place is that they are not fully aware of the benefits. They think they would get a few new patients from their efforts in that area, but they don't see the overall picture of just how lucrative a successful referral system can be.

If given a magic wand that could solve all of their practice problems, most orthodontists would simply ask for more new patients. This leads them down every rabbit hole that promises new patients here, new patients there, new patients everywhere. Too often, however, they completely overlook the patients they already have, and that is a huge mistake. They fail to put a referral system in place that mines the relationships with existing patients for the mutual benefits of both parties. When doctors adequately assess their referral system, they discover some powerful benefits to getting referrals.

First of all, every referral that you get will cut your cost per lead in half. Yes, you can drop your marketing expenditure per new patient by 50 percent every time you get one new patient to refer another one. If you consider how much money your practice spends during the year on advertising, this could add up to some significant savings.

Secondly, your conversion rate on new patients referred by a friend or family member is going to be much higher than a cold prospect or someone who showed up from external marketing or an insurance list. As pointed out before, these are people who are ready to get started with treatment.

Finally, when you build trust, you will build better clients. Patients who trust you will end up spending more, paying in full, and continuing the chain of referrals.

Not having a good understanding of these benefits of getting referrals is the most common reason why doctors don't adequately think through their referral system. After all, why else would any doctor not put in the time to create a great referral system if they knew it would bring them high quality patients who were ready to begin treatment and would help build a better sense of trust among patients?

The most effective way for you to understand the benefits of having a good referral system in place is to actually have one. Once you do that, you will see for yourself what it does for you and your practice. You can always choose to stop doing it or scale back if you feel it's not working for you, but there's no doubt in my mind that you will love the benefits. Not only that, but you will begin to look for ways to make getting referrals a normal part of your entire business. You will begin seeing things in terms of referral opportunities.

> When you build trust, you will build better clients. Patients who trust you will end up spending more, paying in full, and continuing the chain of referrals.

I have worked with many doctors who don't think the effort will be worth the return they get back. Once I've worked with them to get a system in place and things start rolling, they are amazed at how many new patients they get as a result. If you are like other doctors I've worked with, once you see the benefits, you will wonder what took you so long to get started.

BIG GOALS AND ASKING FOR INTRODUCTIONS

Every referral system should have big goals. To achieve these big goals, you must create a referral mindset in your practice. Everyone in the office must know they are in the business of earning trust and referrals. Don't just sit back and wait for referrals to happen. If you do that, you will be losing out on a lot of new patients coming your way. You have to take action in order to make things happen. Go make things happen.

To achieve big goals, you have to take the initiative. That means if you want to establish a relationship with "whales" (owners of companies with lots of employees, members of the school board, leaders in the religious institutions, etc.), you have to ask for the introduction. "I'd love to come by and show your health teachers what we're doing with cleft palate kids," or "Did you know we have shadowing and mentorship programs here? If you have any students

> *When you have a referral mindset and work toward the big goals, you are going to see some big results.*

or kids of employees who want to see what it's like to be an orthodontist, we'd love to have them over to the office. Who is the best person I should reach out to so we can get this started?"

Don't be timid when it comes to asking for introductions. Some people shy away from this type of thing, but it is part of having a successful referral system. You may feel reserved the first couple of times, but you will soon get over that uncomfortable feeling. And when you start seeing results from your efforts, you will be that much more comfortable with asking for introductions.

When you have a referral mindset and work toward the big goals, you are going to see some big results. Consider the myriad ways you can actively plant seeds that will bring you new patients. There are plenty of opportunities around for reaching out to make a connection. From schools to corporations and even groups like the Girl Scouts and Boy Scouts, you can find ways to make connections and encourage people to get information about your office.

Girl Scouts, for example, can earn a dental health patch. Put an invitation out to all of the Girl Scout troops in the area that you are happy to help them earn that patch. While they are visiting your office or you are attending their meeting place, be sure to provide information about your services that can be sent home with each child. Not only will the kids get a chance to meet you, but the leaders will also speak with you. This is a chance to make a small connection with all of them, which may lead to some referrals down the line.

Asking for introductions can be a great way to get your foot in the door of places that can bring you referrals. Don't just go in blindly, though; try to do some homework first so the introduction is more thought out and has a better chance of being a good fit. Determine who you already know who can introduce you to those you'd like to know, or who at the company can introduce you to the appropriate decision-making person. Having the right person making the introduction is an important step because they can provide some much appreciated credibility.

BUILDING TRUST

We know that people refer someone whom they trust. So with that in mind, you want to do things in your practice that will build trust with your patients. One simple thing you can do is to get into the habit of memorizing names and facts about your patients. When you use their first name and can ask them how it's going with their baseball games—or whatever it is that they are into—they will feel that you care about them, and you will be building trust. People refer others to those whom they like and trust. It's just that simple. You won't build trust if you can't greet people by name and make them feel special.

Not only do I advocate memorizing your patients' names, but I have seen the benefits of this myself. My pastor while I was in dental school didn't know my name only *once*—and that was the very first time he met me. It was the same for everyone in the congregation because he made it a point to memorize everyone's name. When I asked him about this great skill later in life, he admitted he hadn't always been that good at it, but had noticed the tremendous results it got him while growing his congregation. He practiced this skill a few hours every week until he got really, really good at remembering names. Now it's like second nature to him. Try it yourself. The results will be amazing.

> One simple thing you can do is to get into the habit of memorizing names and facts about your patients.

Most people I have discussed this topic with realize how important it is to be able to call people by their name. There's no doubt you have experienced it, too. If someone calls you by your name, they are implying that the discussion is important. In other words, *you* are important. They took the time to remember who you are, a huge step in building a trusting relationship with a patient. Even though most people realize the importance of this little task, they often fail to do it. Consider how many times you have heard people claim they are bad at remembering names. It's true that most people start out being bad at names because the vast majority of us are not born with that ability. It's a skill that we have to hone.

With more practice, you will get better at remembering the names of patients and even referral sources. First, you have to want to do it and be committed to sharpening this skill. When you are ready to begin strengthening your name-memorization skills, start out slowly and build as you go along. When you meet someone new or have a patient come in, repeat their name a couple of times throughout the conversation or appointment. Many people find it helps if you can make a mental association with their name. For example, if you find out that Brad likes baseball, that's an association that will help you to remember the name, as well as what it is that Brad likes.

Other tips for improving your name memorization skills include reading it when it's on paper, whether it's on their patient chart, a name tag, or their business card. If you find that someone has a name that is unfamiliar to you or difficult to pronounce, ask them to clarify how to properly pronounce it. That will be much better than just taking a stab at it on your own and totally messing it up. They will appreciate that you care enough to ask them how to pronounce their name.

One of the most important rules when it comes to remembering someone's name is to give them your undivided attention. It's difficult to remember someone's name if you are doing several things at once and not giving them the attention they deserve. Give your patients the courtesy of your attention, looking them in the eye and using their name. These are the things that will establish a connection to your office and help them learn to trust you.

LOSING TRUST

We have talked a lot about the importance of trust when it comes to having a successful referral system. It is without a doubt one of the most important, if not *the* most important, components of the entire system. So what happens when you do something that makes people not trust you, or draws your trust into question?

Warren Buffet once said, "It takes twenty years to build a reputation and five minutes to ruin it." That's exactly the way it works when it comes to trust.

131

It could take you years to build it up. But it could take you only a short time to chip away at it, and you may not even be aware that something is wrong or that you are eroding the trust that people have with your practice. A small trust problem in one area of your practice can have a ripple effect that brings harm to the whole office.

One of the most common reasons practices begin to lose trust is by not providing great customer service. Word-of-mouth is powerful; and if you are not giving people great service, they will talk. If you are giving people less than great service, they are going to talk even more. Research shows that people will talk more about service they were unhappy with than about service they were happy with. So if you make someone unhappy, it is going to reach others, and it can begin to erode your reputation and the trust that people have with your practice.

> *If your practice is called into question for any reason, you should address the issue immediately . . . the public appreciates when companies that have had issues actually address the problems.*

There are other ways you could be losing trust with your patients—or even potential referrals—and you may not even be aware of it. Places this can happen include your website, social media, and brochures. The information provided on those outlets needs to be updated, accurate, and trustworthy. If people are reading the information and they see things that are inaccurate or outdated, they will begin to question your practice.

Not only is it important to be consistent with providing great service and trustworthy information, you also need to address problems immediately when they arise. If your practice is called into question for any reason, you should address the issue immediately. People appreciate when others are honest, open, and apologetic for things they may have mishandled. And the public appreciates when companies that have had issues actually address the problems. This is an area where you don't want to remain silent and ignore the problem, hoping that it will go away.

If issues arise, be sure to address them, correct the problem, and then move forward, focusing on more positive aspects and providing great service. Letting people know you see there is a problem and letting them know what you are doing to correct it will go a long way toward rebuilding that trust again. Damage control, as many refer to it in the business world, is addressing the problems that may exist, but trying to control the image with it so that it doesn't destroy your practice in the long run.

Practices that have serious issues, such as lawsuits or problems that have made their way into the media, should bring a professional on board. By working with a public relations expert, you will be able to do damage control that will not only help you address the problems, but will strategically help your image through the issues and beyond. They can help you think through the short and long term about how to best address the problems and rebuild trust once again.

NOT DOING THE WORK

There's another important reason why many doctors don't have a referral system in place. It simply comes down to the fact that they don't want to do the work. In all honesty, setting up a referral system is going to take some time and effort on your part. But without it, you are leaving so much money on the table, and you are keeping your practice from growing. If you put in the time and effort to create the system, without a doubt, you will reap the rewards.

If you do a comparison of how much time, effort, and money you will need to invest to create a referral system for your practice, you can use that information and compare it to what you will lose by *not* bringing in those referrals. Let's say your office can comfortably start out bringing in ten new referrals per month and that each one is worth $5,000 of profit after they have completed treatment. That's $50,000 per month. The investment you will put into starting the referral system—including time, effort, and funds—will pale in comparison to what you will pass up if you don't do it. Starting and maintaining a successful referral system is always worth it.

> Setting up a referral system is going to take time and effort, but without it, you are leaving money on the table.

Creating the referral system may seem like a huge thing to get started, but don't feel overwhelmed. If you do, it will likely make you run the other direction; and you will be missing out on all those new patients. Instead keep a list of everything you want to include in your referral system, and then include a time frame for when you'd like to get each of these things in place. You don't have to get everything done overnight, but you don't want to take six months to do it either. Aim to get everything in place within 90 days. Once you have it going, keep working at it and fine tune what you feel needs to be adjusted. After a while, it will be working like a well-oiled machine.

Having a successful referral system doesn't have to be overwhelming or overly time-consuming, especially if you get others in your team on board to help. Your office staff is a team all working toward the same goal, so there's no reason not to empower your team members to be a part of your referral system. There are numerous good reasons to do so, and chances are your team will appreciate being a part of helping the office to grow.

FEAR OF FAILURE

There are plenty of doctors who understand the importance of a referral system, yet they don't move forward with putting one in place. This is because of the fear of failure. They fear the system will not work for them after putting in all the time, effort, and funds to create it; and all of their efforts will have been wasted. So many people are too paralyzed to move forward because they are either complacent or fear their efforts won't pay off.

There *are* people who put forth at least some effort to create a referral system only to have it fail. Of course, not everyone is going to be successful just because they have created what they are calling a referral system. There are some common reasons why referral systems fail.

One reason—and it's not the fault of the referral system itself—is because the service that is offered isn't good. Let's consider for a moment what would happen if you put the effort into creating a referral system, only to provide boring or mediocre service to the patients who did come in. How many of those people do you think would go on to refer others? There's a good chance that even though you had thought through your referral system and had many things in place, you didn't go all the way in making sure you were providing excellent, above-average service to those who did come into your office.

Another reason that some people don't have the success they want with their referral system is that they missed something, such as having good collateral materials, for example. It's important to have good content and materials available for people to give out freely and often to bring in referrals. If you don't have good information readily available for people to hand out, you have a hole in your referral system that will keep it weak. Fill that gap by getting some useful and professional content that can be distributed on a regular basis.

I've also come across a few doctors who felt their referral system was working some of the time, but not all of the time. When I discuss the issue with them, what we usually find is that the referral system is being used in an inconsistent manner. If you and your team are only using it part-time, it stands to reason that you can only expect to get part-time results. To have a referral system that works well all year long, you have to use it—*all* the time. You must consistently follow the system you put in place to see the benefits you want.

Additionally, people may end up not getting their expected results from their referral system because they are not tapping their referral resources enough. If you have a good referral source, don't stop with getting one referral from them. One-and-done methods of getting referrals will keep you busy, but you will be leaving many quality referrals behind. When you see that you have a good referral source, continue to tap it on a regular basis, making that source a special priority. Forget one-and-done and focus on going for the gusto so you can minimize your efforts and maximize your referrals.

FEARS AND DELUSIONS

Beyond the fear of the whole referral system not working, there are some doctors who are afraid to ask for referrals. They feel their service should speak for itself and that they shouldn't have to mention that they would appreciate referrals. Being afraid of asking people for referrals can not only kill your referral system, but it can seriously harm your practice. You have to get over that fear and see that there is nothing wrong with asking for referrals. And if your patients are happy with your services, they will appreciate your telling them you are happy to get referrals. Perhaps they just haven't thought about it before, but they love the idea of telling others about your office. That little nudge can make a huge difference for your practice.

You may not have thought about it before, but if they are honestly happy with your services, your patients will also be happy to help you out by referring you. In your line of work, you are already getting most of your new patients from referrals, but you just haven't put in much effort thus far into making it happen. All you are doing by losing the fear is focusing on getting more referrals. Be afraid of the patients you may be losing by *not* engaging in solid referral tactics.

TESTIMONIALS COUNT

Have you ever thought about getting written testimonials from some of your patients who are happy with your services? Having testimonials is another form of word-of-mouth referrals, because you are getting those patients to write down what they like about your office or their treatment outcome. You can use short snippets where they are giving your office a stamp of approval. Add them to your website, post them on social media, and even use them in brochures that focus on particular types of treatment. Those real testimonials will be helpful to those reading your treatment content, especially if they can see themselves in the person sharing the testimonial. People see themselves in testimonials if they are going through a similar situation, share the same concerns before treatment, are around the same age, etc.

Getting testimonials from your satisfied patients is easier than you may think. Again, I point out that satisfied patients are happy to help you and won't have a problem giving you a testimonial. All you need to do is get their permission to have a written testimonial attributed to their name, and then ask them a few questions to get the information. Some of the questions you will want to ask include what fears they may have had prior to treatment, what they like best about the way their treatment turned out, what the best thing about going to your office for the treatment was, and whether there is anything else they would like to share.

Chances are you will get far more information for the testimonial than you will actually want to use. Testimonials do not need to be lengthy. In fact, they should be on the shorter side because the majority of people are not going to take the time to read lengthy ones. People prefer to read short pieces—perhaps just a paragraph—that offer the most important information. So edit down the original testimonial to a short paragraph without changing the writer's overall thoughts.

> Getting testimonials from your satisfied patients is easier than you may think. All you need to do is get their permission to have a written testimonial attributed to their name, and then ask them a few questions to get the information.

Although you will largely want to stick to shorter pieces for testimonials, it is also okay to consider sharing longer patient success stories here and there. These longer pieces go into more detail about the person's treatment experience and outcome and can be used on social media channels, in promotional pieces, and as additional content on your website or blog. Try to pair patient stories with a photo of the patient so people can make a connection to the person and treatment.

If you use video promotion, you can also get video testimonials where the patient is interviewed. Just be sure the videos are edited so they look professional. Add them to your own YouTube channel, or create a video section on your blog or website. These promotional videos can also be posted to social media. To create an effective video, focus on one type of treatment. Optional shots to include in the video are images of your office, video of your staff or you discussing the treatment, and a short clip from one of your patients who will be providing the testimonial.

TESTIMONIAL BENEFITS

When you add testimonials to your referral system, you will have built-in, word-of-mouth referrals from people on hand and ready to go. Testimonials benefit your practice in much the same way as any other type of referral. They help establish trust. Having the testimonials prepared ahead of time and ready for delivery to people doesn't diminish the trust-building benefits they offer. And they are not seen as sales pitches, because it's not your office saying the information in the testimonials; it's coming from an actual person in your community, rather than someone from your practice. Testimonials help people overcome any skepticism they may have about going forward with treatment.

Be wise when choosing which testimonials to use in your content. Remember, you need them to help sell your services to those reading or watching them. Good testimonials will include the person sharing the benefits of the treatment as well as something that people reading or watching it can relate to. Good testimonials will also support your treatment guarantee, recommend your services, and be honest and credible.

There are some people who create bogus testimonials, but I urge you not to engage in such this behavior. Get the testimonials from real people in your community. Be sure to include each person's first and last name and their city. If your layout allows, add a picture of the person, too. If a testimonial addresses the fact that your patient had considered others—your competitors—but opted to go with you instead, have them explain what helped them make that decision.

Always get permission to use testimonials, and never edit what they said in order to make it sound better. Keep them all honest and real. Testimonials are only as good as the quality that went into creating them. Determine which patients you should ask to provide a testimonial, and then work to ensure that a beneficial one is constructed and strategically used.

WHAT TO DO

Most doctors don't adequately think through their referral system. There is a lot involved in understanding the importance of referrals and creating a successful referral system. But the good news is that putting in the effort is well worth it in the long run. Having a referral system will bring you the new patients you need to help your business succeed and grow.

Once you understand this about referral systems, the only thing that remains is what you should do about it, including how you should move forward with implementing your own. Tony Robbins said, "The path to success is to take massive, determined action." That's exactly what every doctor should do once they have decided they are going to have a referral system in place. Without taking action to make it happen and bringing it all together, your system will go nowhere, and there's a good chance your practice won't grow.

The first step in having a great referral system is to learn all you can about what's included in one, which is what is covered in this book. The next step is to put it into action, creating a plan for what you need to do and when you will do it. The final step is to actually get it started. You can always make adjustments as you go along and see things that should be added, changed, or dropped. Taking action to put everything you learn in this book into play should be a major goal, and one you hold yourself accountable to complete. Only by taking determined action will you begin to see the level of success you crave from a referral system.

CHAPTER TWELVE

WORKING WITH REFERRING DENTISTS

When is the last time you got into your car and drove around to visit dentists' offices in your area so you could ask them for referrals? Most orthodontists will admit, at least privately, that they hate going around from dental office to dental office begging for referrals. So if that's you, then know you are not alone. But it is something you will need to rethink if you want to have success in the world of referrals. As I've explained many times before, referrals are largely based on relationships. And you have to actively build those relationships to get the referrals.

RELATIONSHIPS MATTER

Most doctors see asking others for referrals as beneath them, or they see it as groveling for their future success. I don't see it this way at all. Life is a relationships business. Whether it's your butcher, baker, or candlestick maker, you ought to learn how to build relationships with everyone around you so both parties can mutually benefit. Knowing that most vendors, employees, business partners and referring dentists will eventually go "lame" on you, it's not a game you ever finish playing. If you want to be successful, you will be in a perpetual relationship-building mode until the day they put you in the ground.

Even if dentists don't refer to you, it is your job to maintain a relationship with anyone who might see one of your patients. I have a great referring dentist who will never send me a patient in her life—and I don't blame her. Both her father and brother are orthodontists, so it's understandable that they get her referrals. But we still maintain a good working relationship with this dentist because she has a popular practice, and so do I. We see a lot of the same patients, even though they are never referred to me. We have to maintain a good relationship so I can give her what she needs for implant cases, pre-restorative ortho cases, etc. I still work on that relationship, even though most orthodontists would write it off as a waste of time.

Relationships are the building blocks of all the repeat business we do. Sure, we may try something once—not knowing the source or the person providing the service—but we only continue to keep going back if we build a relationship. When you build relationships with the dentists in your area, you will automatically begin getting more referrals from them. They will know you, trust you, like you, and want to send their patients to you.

REFERRALS CHANGE

An important thing to remember about referrals is that things will change over time. The referral pattern you establish now will most likely not be the same five years from now. Referral patterns change. Some of the best business relationships in the world either weren't in place five years ago, or will be dissolved within the next five years. Businesses come and go. They open and close, and they move around. That's just the nature of things in the business world, and these changes are going to influence your referral patterns.

The fact that businesses come and go doesn't mean you don't mine the relationship for the mutual benefit of both parties while you can. Too many doctors want everything to be perfect, to be written in stone and never change. That doesn't explain life at all. Change how you approach this and you will see that it works to your benefit. If you can roll with the changes and continuously adapt your plan to it, you will have no problem keeping up and staying ahead.

Someone who isn't sending referrals to you now may very well start in the future when they become dissatisfied with their current orthodontic referral preference, or if that doctor closes, retires, or relocates. Other dentists are coming into the market while some are retiring. Your referral patterns will typically change entirely every five to seven years, so you must be in perpetual recruitment mode. Keep a list of ten dentists who are not currently referring to you and have your TC, office manager, you, or all of you go to their office to offer lunch and learn programs. Bring goodies and send X-rays of the highest quality, letting them know you'd love to see a few of their most difficult cases just so you can show them what you can do.

PAY ATTENTION

It is important to pay close attention when you do get a referral from a dentist. Treat this like the test that it is. Dentists may test you out by sending a patient so they can see how it goes. The outcome for that particular patient may help determine whether or not you get future referrals. Play your cards right, and you may have a steady source of referrals from that dentist; but play them wrong, and there's little chance you will get any more at all.

When dentists do refer a patient to you for the first time, pay attention and make sure everyone on your team knows the importance of this referral and pays attention, too. Deliver what you say you will deliver on-time or early and with the highest quality and respect for how their office works. If they want digital communication emailed to them securely, do it. If they want paper communication sent via postal service, do that. None of this may be how you think it should work, but what you think is right and how the world actually operates are often two different things.

With this first patient the dentist refers to you, be sure to go all out to provide them with the best possible service. You should be doing this for your patients anyway, regardless of where they come from or who referred them, but even more so when it's from a new referring dentist. Also, be sure to take the time to thank the referring dentist. Those thank-you acknowledgements which are often overlooked are actually quite important. Everyone likes to feel appreciated, so take the time to give them your appreciation.

When you get a new patient referred to your office from a dentist who hasn't sent you anyone before, you want to acknowledge that in a big way. Send them a thank-you gift that will get their attention, and be sure to include a handwritten note thanking them and letting them know you appreciate that

The referral pattern you establish now will most likely not be the same five years from now. Referral patterns change.

they thought of your office to send their patient to. Doing little things like this will go a long way toward getting more referrals from that dentist.

GETTING MORE REFERRING DENTISTS

You may be thinking that it sounds great to have some referring dentists, but you don't know where to start getting them. Or perhaps you have a couple of them, but your office could really benefit from having more. If you want to grow your business, you need to have connections with several referring dentists. This is going to increase the number of people coming into your office.

It may seem difficult getting your foot in the door at a dentist office and making sure you are on their radar for referrals; but if they don't know about your office or what you can do for their patients, they simply can't refer you. If you know they already refer to someone else, don't let that stop you from making those connections. As I mentioned already, the referral world is constantly in flux. You may find that they have someone they refer to today, but three months from now they will be looking for someone new to try out or perhaps something may happen to the office they currently recommend. There are many variables that come into play, so it's always a good idea to focus on building the relationship, even if you don't think you will get a return on it immediately—or maybe ever.

When you have made the decision to get more dentists who will refer to you, you need to start making connections with the dentists in your area. Start by making a list of them and identify where each of their offices is located. Then use that list to start making connections. There are many ways to start getting to remember your name, but the one they will remember the most is your dropping in to meet them personally.

If you decide to drop into the dentist offices, be sure to avoid going empty handed. Remember, there is a team of people working in the office and each of them has the ability to refer people to your office, even if it's just in passing when someone asks if they know of a good orthodontist in the area. Everyone you meet in those offices is a chance to get your name put on their office radar, so make the most of it.

When you show up at the dentist offices, be sure to take something with you—perhaps bagels and coffee, lunch, or other fun things they can each keep. Also, make sure you give them some of your brochures and let them know what sets you apart from your competitors. You may want to consider having a brochure made that is intended for dentist offices, explaining what sets you apart, what your track record is, and how you can help their patients.

Consider holding some lunch and learn events, where you invite dental office staff to come have lunch and listen to you share information . . . or your yearly talk on the "state of the industry."

While you may not want to wear out your welcome by going back into that office too often, there is nothing wrong with stopping in a few times a year. You can also help keep your practice on their minds by sending them things, whether it's having a lunch catered for them, dropping off a sweet surprise near Valentine's Day to let them know you love referrals, or by creating a newsletter that goes out to just dentist offices in your area. Additionally, consider holding some lunch and learn events, where you invite dental office staff to come have lunch and listen to you share information about a new procedure, how to address some of their most challenging patient problems, or your yearly talk on the "state of the industry." Each of these things will garner some interest by those in the dental field, and each of them is another opportunity to help make a connection.

ADDITIONAL NETWORKING

Napoleon Hill once said, "It is literally true that you can succeed best and quickest by helping others to succeed." After spending years interviewing and studying what makes people successful, he concluded that this was one of the many secrets to success. We can use this guidance in our field as well. When we help others, good things naturally come to us. Perhaps you can use this to look for ways you can help other dentists, because they will help you in turn.

Everyone has heard about the many virtues of networking, but it bears repeating. When you network, you make connections and lay the foundation for having a relationship. When you have a relationship, you have a much better chance of getting referrals. Therefore, it is advantageous to look for ways you can network with the dentists and the hygienists in your area. Perhaps you can join some local groups, attend functions, or plan your own events to give you the opportunity to meet these people and speak with them. Then the relationship can blossom from there.

Look for every chance you can to connect with the dentists in your area. If you don't, you will probably not be the one they think of when they have a patient who needs to see an orthodontist. Not only do you need to meet these people and get to know them on a first-name basis, but they need to learn about your skills and how you can help their patients—and they need to learn to trust you. You want them to like you and respect what you do so they think of you when they need to refer some of their patients.

Take a look at your current networking efforts to see where you could—and should—make some changes. If you are not networking with dentists in your area, it's time to step up your game and make it a priority to start. Networking is easy and can help you build the foundation for the relationships you need to start getting referrals from those dentists. Even if there are dentists who will never send you referrals because they already have someone they send them to, it's a good idea to make the connection and help them build a favorable opinion of you and your office. You never know when they may be speaking to others about your office, and you want those words to be positive.

KEEPING YOUR REFERRING DENTISTS

Getting referral dentists is one aspect of the equation, but that is not all of it. Once you have them, you have to work to keep them. Not just to keep the people being referred to you, but you need to work to keep that dentist as someone who continues to refer to you for the long haul. Once you get that first referral from a dentist, you have to recognize that this is just the beginning of the relationship. Like all good relationships, you will have to work at keeping that relationship good, too.

It is important to keep in mind that referring dentists can decide to stop referring their patients to you at any time. It might be either an abrupt or gradual change, but they could start sending their patients elsewhere whenever they choose. Every time they send you a referral, they have made the conscious decision to do so because they feel you are the right fit for their patient. Therefore, every time they sent you a referral, you should show gratitude that they chose you—whether it's their first referral or they've been sending referrals for years.

You express that gratitude by thanking them each and every time they send you a referral. I have talked to numerous doctors in my consulting experience who let the dentist know they appreciated that first referral, but then moved on and didn't express any gratitude after that. They didn't think it was necessary to continue to thank the dentist for each referral after that first one.

In my practice, we look at this differently. We are grateful for every referral a dentist sends to us, so we acknowledge every one of them. Our follow-up and acknowledgement plan includes a variety of ways to express our gratitude. One time we may send a thank-you note, while another time I may stop in the office to say thank you in person. Other times we may send over a lunch or some gift cards. We try to be creative and look for ways to continue to say thank you, but we don't want it to get old because we're doing the same thing every time. In other words, we don't want to send the same letter telling them thank you every time, because after a while, they likely won't even bother to look at it anymore. They could become so programmed at getting the same thing each time, there is a good chance it would no longer spark their interest.

> Be creative in putting together a wide variety of ways to show gratitude to your referring dentists.

Be creative in putting together a wide variety of ways to show gratitude to your referring dentists. You don't have to go way out and do something huge every time, but doing so once a year for those who continually refer people to you is a good idea. The point is you should acknowledge every referral you get in some way. What you do specifically to show gratitude for each referral is not the focus here. The most important thing to remember is that you should show gratitude for every patient who is referred to you.

When a dentist refers someone to your office, in a sense, they have vouched for your office. They have said to their trusted patient that they believe you will do a good job and you will further their treatment in a successful manner. This is not something you should take lightly. Out of every orthodontist in your area, they trusted you with their patient—and ultimately their own reputation. Be grateful and let them know you appreciate their thinking so highly of your office and that you won't let them down.

Showing appreciation for the referrals you get is one way to keep getting them, but there are other things you will want to do as well. The other big one is how you treat the patient. It should go without saying that it is important to treat the patient who the dentist has referred to you for treatment well. *Really* well. That patient is going to go back to their dentist and will report how it went at your office.

Patients referred by dentists need to experience more than just successful treatment. While they absolutely need successful treatment results—which will demonstrate your skill and expertise—they also need to have an overall good experience at your office. Avoid downplaying how important it is to patients that they be acknowledged and treated kindly, and that your team shows genuine interest in them being there. Whatever type of experience it is that they have at your office, the patient is going to go back to their dental office and share with the dentist—and possibly others on the team—how their visit went with you. You want them to offer a favorable report so the dentist continues to feel good about sending you more of their patients. If for some reason patients were to give them a negative report, they would begin to second guess sending you referrals. So focus on providing an excellent patient experience from beginning to end, not only so that the person will tell others about you, but because you want the patient to give their dentist a positive report.

THE RESEARCH

Research has been conducted on why it is that dentists refer their patients to specific orthodontists. In the journal "*The Angle Orthodontist*," researchers randomly surveyed 1,000 general dentists in America's Midwest to find out what made them choose one orthodontist over another for their referrals. What they found from the results of the survey was that 75 percent said quality of previous orthodontic treatment and patient/parental satisfaction were of equal importance in their referral decision.

This means that the top two reasons why dentists refer to particular orthodontists are the quality of the treatment provided and how well the patient and their parent (if the patient was a minor) was treated at the office. These two things overwhelmingly topped any of the other reasons that someone may choose a specific orthodontist office, including the location of the orthodontist's office, the orthodontist's reputation, or the anticipated cost of the treatment.

Researchers concluded that since the decision on which orthodontist a dentist refers patients to comes down to a couple of interactive decisions, it's a good idea for orthodontists to always provide high-quality treatment, interact well with patients and their family members, and maintain good communication with general practitioners in the community.

To put it plainly, what a referring dentist wants is for the orthodontist to provide high-quality treatment, be nice to the people, and keep in contact with the dentist's office. It's just that simple. As long as you keep that in mind and make the effort, you will be opening doors to getting more dentist referrals—and keeping them.

This information is based off a survey of 1,000 dentists, but you can even do your own research, too. It's not a bad idea to make contact with the dentists in your area and ask them what it is they look for when they refer. Find out what is important to them, and then make every effort to provide that. There is a good chance you will reach the same conclusion these researchers did. Dentists want to refer to an orthodontist who does a good job providing treatment, treats patients well, and communicates with their office. That's the simple formula, and it's one that every orthodontist can do.

ROLLING WITH THE CHANGES

The world is fluid, so things are changing constantly. Once you've taken the time to set up your referral system, things will change. But don't spend too much time worrying about that, because when things change, you will simply need to change along with it. Adapt to those changes and go with the flow. Forget about trying to hold on tightly to whatever system it is you set up in the beginning. You don't want to make things so rigid that you are boxed in; that would prevent you from expanding your reach and being able to adapt to changes.

As dentists leave—regardless of the reasons—they will be replaced with new dentists. Over the course of your practice, you will find there is an ebb and flow; and patients and referring dentists will come and go over the years. That's okay. Just go with it as long as it is still working and bringing you a steady stream of referrals. The only time you need to become concerned is when the referrals are dropping, you are not meeting your goals each month or year, or if dentists are still in business and they are just choosing to refer their patients to someone else. Those are all red flags you will want to investigate and find a solution for. If a dentist stops sending you referrals, inquire about the reason why because you can't fix a problem you don't know about.

Your local dentists can be some of the most important tools for growing your business. Many orthodontists I've worked with launch their practice and then immediately forget about the dentists in their area. When you do that, you are passing up a goldmine for helping your practice. Dentists are usually the first stop for people who will need your services. You want to be the first orthodontist they think of when they have a patient who needs a referral. But you can't become that referral source without putting in some effort and making a name for yourself with each of them. It's well worth the effort to do so and essential to having a successful referral system for your practice.

> *Dentists are usually the first stop for people who will need your services. You want to be the first orthodontist they think of when they have a patient who needs a referral.*

If you haven't made much of an effort thus far to get to know the dentists in your area, now is the time to get the wheels in motion. You want every dentist in your area to know who you are, how good you are at what you do, and why they should choose your office over the competition. Make a plan, reach out to them, and keep reaching out to them. Your efforts will pay off. Focus on laying the foundation for building relationships so they trust you and send patients your way. Once they do that, they will continue to send you more if you provide those patients with great treatment and service.

CHAPTER THIRTEEN

WORKING WITH REFERRING PHYSICIANS

IF YOU ARE LIKE MOST OTHER ORTHODONTISTS, YOU ASSUME THAT THE ONLY OTHER DOCTOR you are likely to get a referral from are the dentists in your area. I've consulted with plenty of orthodontists who felt the same way. They had their focus set on the dentists in their area and never gave much thought to what opportunities may lay beyond those. Just like I have told others I've worked with, I want you to think about working with referring physicians.

This is an overlooked category of referrals that most orthodontists never think about. My practices see tons of patients referred by pediatricians, ENTs, family practitioners, allergists, plastic surgeons, and neurologists. If you haven't approached these potential referral sources with information that could help their patients, you are missing out on a huge opportunity.

WHO TO CONSIDER

When you think about the number of physicians in your area and begin to see how they could each become an ally in your quest to get referrals, you should start to get excited. Most likely, this is an untapped source of referrals because most orthodontists don't even think to make a connection with these physicians, so it leaves the field wide open for you. There are plenty of opportunities; you just need to look around and develop a mindset that helps you look at each physician's office as a potential referral source. Would it make sense? Is it possible?

More often than not, I would say that establishing the relationship does make sense. Every physician in your area is a potential referral source. It's time to begin looking at them through new eyes—referral eyes. Here are a few of your best physician opportunities for getting referrals.

Pediatricians

Consider the number of people in your community who are under the age of 18. There are a lot of them, and many are seeing a pediatrician on a regular basis, whether it's for immunizations, an annual physical, or an illness. Families rely upon their pediatrician for a wide variety of information to help keep their kids healthy and developing well. Some common issues they may routinely inquire about include thumb sucking, pacifier usage, ear infections, and cleft palate. Rather than leave it up to the pediatrician to find information on these common issues, provide the information for them. Come up with a list of possible topics about which you can have professional informational articles written. When this is turned into a nice informational piece that the pediatrician can offer to their patients, you have made their job easier. And of course, each promotional brochure will have your office listed, along with your contact information.

ENTs

Most of the ear, nose, and throat doctors I know love to provide people with information about expansion, mouth breathing, tonsils, and adenoids—as it relates to orthodontic treatment and airway—as well as frequent ear infections and cleft palate cases. Provide them with reports and articles (i.e., referral tools) they can hand out to their patients, and they will send you patients. You can provide helpful treatment to more of their patients than you may have realized initially.

Family Practitioners

These doctors see a wide variety of patients, ranging from the youngest to the oldest and everyone in between. Family practitioners like to be able to provide information for teens and adults about the effects of orthodontic treatment on self-esteem and alternatives to traditional metal braces, such as SureSmile, Invisalign, and Lingual orthodontics. Provide them with the information on technology so they can pass it along to their patients—and they will pass patients along to you.

Plastic Surgeons

Plastic surgeons have an obvious tie-in with our cleft palate foundation—and with orthognathic surgery cases—but they can also send adult patients who have underlying skeletal dysplasia in addition to soft tissue concerns. Find a good plastic surgeon to make a connection with, and you can help a tremendous number of patients in this niche. Plastic surgeons also come in contact with many people who are concerned with their appearance and in making improvements. Those people may appreciate information on what your services can do to help them in this area and to boost their confidence level. Many people who visit plastic surgeons may also want to consider braces, so be sure to provide them with the type of information they can give to their patients.

Neurologists and Pain Specialists

Finally, neurologists and pain specialists are great resources to connect with TMD patients, if you treat this subset. You can be of assistance here and get referrals by providing articles, books, and resources that these specialists can provide to their patients. This will help you establish your expertise with this group and should result in referrals coming your way. Many people don't even realize the oral connection to the pain they are experiencing and that they can get some comfort with the right orthodontic treatment.

All of these physicians may potentially need an orthodontist to refer their patients to on occasion. Whether they have the potential to send you one referral per month or one per day, you want to be the one they are sending the referrals to when the need arises.

Every physician in your area is a potential referral source. It's time to begin looking at them through new eyes—referral eyes.

Put together a list of possible physicians for you to target in your local area. Even if they are on the other side of town, you will want to include them in your list. As I mentioned earlier, you may be the only orthodontist looking to build a connection with these doctors, so you have a good chance of getting in and creating a relationship.

Providing these places with information they can hand out to their patients is honestly a no-brainer. There is no doubt you should take the time to do it because it will always be worth the effort and should provide a nice return on investment.

You may even know people who can help you make the introduction. If you have mutual friends with someone you would like to meet regarding referral opportunities, don't hesitate to ask for the introduction. If you can be introduced by that mutual friend, it will automatically help you break through the first layer and you will be trusted more from the start. There can be big benefits from an introduction based on a mutual friendship.

KNOWING THE RULES

If you are going to speak to physicians and their employees, be sure you are aware of the laws in your state. Most doctors are no longer allowed to receive any gifts at all, even lunch, after the questionable practices of many pharmaceutical companies that were giving gifts and lavish dinners with expensive wines and meals to doctors. The doctors were in turn being pressured to prescribe one medication over another.

This became such a heated issue that the government passed the Sunshine Act, requiring pharmaceutical companies to now report any payments, gifts, or other services given to doctors that have a value over $10. It's estimated that the pharmaceutical companies were spending over $20 billion on these gifts each year, and then they would track the prescribing habits of the doctors to determine if they had a good return on investment. Of course, doctors who were receiving the great incentives were bound to prescribe that company's medications more often than competing brands.

Having said this, don't use it as an excuse not to go speak to physicians, but be aware of what you are and are *not* allowed to bring with you. We typically send a cover letter, a few sample reports that have no marketing message in the report—just great content—and an opportunity for them to schedule a presentation with their employees. You will find that the doctors and their staff are often receptive to hearing what you have to say and obtaining information

> *Most doctors are no longer allowed to receive any gifts at all. . . be aware of what you are and are **not** allowed to bring with you.*

from you that they can hand out to their patients. Nurse practitioners, for example, love to have resources (e.g., pamphlets, books, reports, articles, etc.) that they can hand out to parents who have questions about any of the topics discussed in this chapter.

When you are trying to get to know the doctors in your area, there may even be some who are a little uncomfortable about you showing up bearing gifts, so it's not necessarily a bad thing to come without any. Just being able to get to know them and provide them with quality information they can give out to their patients works wonders, and it's a win-win for everyone involved. Their patients get the information they need from a trusted source, the doctor has helped to get the information the patient needed, and you will end up getting some referrals out of it.

MAKING THE CONNECTION

There are several different ways you can make a connection with the physicians in your area. You may prefer to start off by contacting the one you feel most comfortable with. We usually make our first contact with physicians by sending them informational materials, like the ones I mentioned before. This opens the door and gives us something to bring up once we meet in person. I can always ask if the doctor has a moment to look over the reports that my office previously sent to them.

You can also opt for just stopping in the office during non-peak times to see if you can meet the doctor and make the introduction. This is a good idea because you can meet them in person, which makes the introduction more memorable. But you also risk them being busy and you're pulling them away from their work. Another option is to attend some of the same networking functions they go to, make the introduction, and then follow that up by sending them information in the mail.

The most important first step you can take to get referrals from the physicians in your area is to open the line of communication. Once you have done that, find out what will assist them in helping their patients the most. With their permission, provide them with the right tools that they can use to provide their patients with information. Once they begin giving these informational materials out to their patients, they will likely send you referrals. From there, the key to getting more referrals is to provide high quality treatment and great patient service to them and their family.

Whatever you do, don't be nice to the teen in your chair and forget to be nice to the parent sitting in the waiting room, too. The family members in tow need the same nice treatment. Oftentimes, they have a say in where the child or teen is going for treatment and they will most certainly share their opinion of you and your office with the referring doctor, friends, and others in the community.

QUALITY TOOLS

One of the things I have always striven to do with my practice is to provide patients with a wide variety of information. These tools, as I like to call them, are an important part of growing my practice. If there is a particular treatment I want to let people know about—or I'd like to get more patients to administer it to—then I create the information that is needed to help me do that. From brochures and articles to everything in between, I have a wide variety of marketing tools that serve the purpose of providing people with the information they need. And in turn, these tools encourage more people to opt for those treatments.

There are plenty of options to choose from when putting together your collection of informational marketing tools. Consider the possibilities available, including articles, books, pamphlets, reports, guest blog posts, brochures, and more. The important thing here is to tailor the information to your audience. Consider the office where it will be distributed so you know who your audience is, then have it created to speak specifically to that market.

Let's consider a pediatrician in your area whom you would like to start working with for referrals. What can you provide to that pediatrician that they can use to help their patients? Quite a bit, actually. Here are just a few ideas of what could be created for pediatricians to give to their patients.

- **An article answering the most common questions parents have about thumb-sucking.** Thumb-sucking is an issue nearly every pediatrician gets asked about on a weekly basis. Many parents are worried about what it may do to their child's teeth and wonder what they can do about it.
- **A handy pamphlet answering questions about braces and the options that are out there for their teen.** Many parents are not aware that there are so many options today when it comes to braces, or that treatment can often start at a younger age.
- **A guest blog post or article on the best types of Halloween candy for those with braces.** Many physicians maintain blogs, and they are often open to guest blog posts. You can write periodic guest blog posts with information pertaining to their audience. Answer questions, provide information, and always link it back to your site. This will help push traffic to your own website, but it will also get your name out there so you are being established as an expert in the field and a trusted source.
- **A video about Invisalign they can post on their social media channels.** People watch videos online by the billions. They love them no matter what they are about. Providing a physician with a link to one of your videos on Invisalign—or another treatment—is a good way to get your name in front of their patients. They can post the helpful video link on their social media channels, such as their Facebook page.

- **A brochure containing frequently asked questions (FAQs) about children and orthodontics.** Frequently asked questions brochures are popular with those who want information quickly and want to get to the point. You identify the most common questions and simply answer each one. These FAQ brochures are easy to understand, establish your expertise, and provide people with information about your office.
- **Information in the form of an article or flier that discusses overbites and underbites.** Articles and fliers can be created covering a wide range of topics. They are a great item for getting the information into the hands of those who need it. You can make a list of all of the possible topics that would work, and then determine if an article, flier, or something else would be the best format. There are many possibilities when it comes to articles, which can all be written and designed to look like professional magazine articles. These articles can be attributed to you and include your office information at the end.
- **Any other type of marketing materials that have been developed for their target market.** These can include anything from a custom short magazine offering a variety of articles to rack cards about different types of issues parents may be interested in reading about while at the pediatrician's office.

There are obviously many options for what type of materials to provide, and there are also many different types of physicians to target with the information. When you consider each type of physician, make a list of the various ailments their patients may need corrected by and orthodontist. Not everything will make sense to give to a physician's office. Providing an article about braces options for adults to the pediatrician's office doesn't make sense. But it does for the general practitioner and the cosmetic surgeon. Consider the audience and be sure to target the information you are providing so your efforts will pay off.

While each of these content pieces will have the underlying goal of bringing you referrals, you do not want it to come across as a sales piece. If someone picks it up to read it and it comes across like a sales piece, they will likely lay it right back down and not give it a second thought. What they want and need is information. Provide them with the information they are looking for, and they will grow to trust you.

When you create your marketing pieces, whichever ones they may be, make sure to include your office's contact information, as well as your website address and physical address. Make sure you let them know your office provided the professional information and advice, but don't come across as a salesman. Providing people with helpful content they can read both online and off is a great way to get people to trust you as an expert. The information you provide should be helpful, accurate, and professional.

Many people I have worked with assume they have to find the time to write everything for these informational pieces on their own, as well as do all the graphic work to lay them out. If you are particularly talented in this area and have the extra time, you may want to take on the task. But if you would rather someone else do it, don't hesitate to hire a professional writer and graphic artist to do the work for you. This is what they do for a living, and they can do the work while you are busy doing yours. They will write what you need, making sure it sounds professional, and then do the graphic layout that makes it look great. Then all you have to do is have it printed.

It's always a good idea to have professionals work on these information pieces. Each one of them, after all, is likely the first point of contact a potential new patient will have with your office. Hand them something that is sloppily written and poorly laid out, and your office will be viewed the same way. They will not think very highly of your office, and this type of tool will not help garner trust. On the other hand, provide them with something that looks professional, is professionally written and designed, and offers helpful information, and it will go a long way toward bringing you referrals.

Something that looks professional, is professionally written and designed, and offers helpful information will go a long way toward bringing you referrals.

We have become masters at using materials like this to bring in new referrals to my practices. We have a wide variety of topics presented, and we have presented them in a multitude of ways. Not everyone will pick up an article and read it, but maybe they like to watch videos. I have them covered, no matter what format they like to get the information in. We offer people articles, pamphlets, brochures, videos, blog posts, and more. Our mission is to provide everyone with as much relevant information as we can to help answer their questions; and when they need an orthodontist, our phone is ringing. So far, we have been quite successful with this approach.

KEEPING TRACK

It's one thing to make contact with members of your community, including every dentist and physician, and then to start feeding them information they can provide to their patients. But it's another thing to keep track of all these contacts to put them to good use. It won't do you much good to put all your efforts into compiling their information and making the initial contact if you never follow up. If you drop off a stack of articles at a pediatrician's office and then forget to go back or keep in touch, you can consider that a lost cause.

Referrals are about relationships, so even though you have gotten your foot in the door, you have to keep it there and do some work to maintain the relationship. Rather than becoming overwhelmed trying to remember everyone you have attempted to contact, use customer relationship management (CRM) software. With CRM, you will be able to enter all of the information about each contact into the system and keep track of every interaction you have with them. This will help you avoid having to rely only on your memory, and it will keep the history of your interactions. CRM can also provide you with reports, updates, and even reminders—automating most of the process.

By keeping track of all of your interactions with CRM, you will be able to see what is working and what isn't. It's a great tool for tracking your efforts and helping you see what is giving you a good return on investment. You can also use it to store little pieces of trivia about a particular office, such as if they only like one particular type of information to be brought to them, if they are open for guest posts for their blog every third Tuesday, or if the doctor is allergic to dairy. (It would be especially helpful to have that note about the allergy so you avoid sending any small gifts that may contain the offending ingredient).

Ideally, you will want to familiarize yourself with the CRM so you have easy access to the information when and where you need it. You can add info, as well as extract it as necessary. It's also a good idea to train at least one other person on your staff in how to use the software so they can also input information or obtain it as needed. That way the people in your office can enter things they learn or feedback they receive into the system right away. A team approach to using CRM is ideal; but at the minimum, you and one other person in your office should be using it regularly to build a useful database of contact information.

PLANTING SEEDS

With each physician you make contact with, you have planted a seed. When you plant a seed—depending on the type of seed it is—it usually doesn't sprout up overnight. They take time to germinate and grow. The same holds true with the seeds you will be planting with each office you contact. Don't make your connections and then kick back in your seat, expecting the referral calls to begin rolling in the next day. That's not how it usually happens.

The truth about referrals and having a successful referral system is that you need to have multiple approaches going on at once, and you need to be patient for them to begin to take hold. Your job is to plant seeds in many areas. You *will* begin to see an effects from it, but it will be over time. If you invest the time in setting it up properly, without a doubt you will end up having a steady supply of referrals coming your way. And the good news is that they will be coming from a variety of sources, rather than from just one or two.

We plant the seeds, water them over time with communication and keeping in contact, and then watch the referral calls roll in. And they *will* roll in. The ultimate goal is to build relationships with these people you are contacting so that they trust you and want to refer people to you. But building relationships isn't something that happens overnight. Any relationship you have ever had is something that has taken time and effort. The same is true with the referral system. Over time, you will have built relationships that strengthen your referral system and help grow your business.

I have had other orthodontists ask me if they should attempt to make a connection with a physician who already has an orthodontist they refer their patients to. Some are concerned, whether or not they personally know the other orthodontist. Even if you know that a physician has one specific orthodontist they refer their patients to, it is still a good idea to make the introduction and get to know them. You never know when circumstances may change and they may be looking for someone else to refer patients to, or when they may be speaking to someone about local orthodontists in particular. It's never a bad idea for local physicians to have a positive attitude and opinion about your office because you never know who they are going to be talking to.

If you know the doctor already has an orthodontist they refer to, you don't want to make it seem as though you are trying to take over that coveted position. But you do want to make the initial connection and keep their information in your CRM. And there's no harm in also adding them to your mailing list so they stay updated and you remain on their radar. You can still network with physicians even if they have someone else they currently refer to—or even if they say they have no need to ever refer their patients at all. Circumstances change all the time, and you want to be the one they think of when they do.

You can create an unlimited flow of referrals coming to your office. You first have to make the commitment to create a referral system, complete the tasks that laid the groundwork to make it successful, then do what it takes to maintain that system you worked so hard to build and perfect. Nobody said it would be easy, but it will be completely worth it. A well-built referral system is the absolute best way to grow your practice. It's also the best use of funds because maintaining your referral system will be much more affordable than managing a large yearly advertising budget. You will find, too, that with your referral system humming along on autopilot, you get a far better return on investment over any of your other marketing and advertising expenses.

> You can create an unlimited flow of referrals coming to your office. . . with your referral system humming along on autopilot. You get a far better return on investment over any of your other marketing and advertising expenses.

THE BEST WAY

As you are learning throughout the pages of this book, if you want to have a steady flow of new patients and grow your practice, establishing and maintaining a good referral system is the number one thing you can do to help your practice. The good news is that it is also something you can start at any time. You don't have to wait for a particular day, month or year to arrive for you to get started growing your business.

There are many reasons why so many people are turning their efforts toward creating a referral system to reach their business goals. One of the best reasons is that you can always track and verify your efforts. When you put money into advertising or marketing, you most likely don't track to see what your return is so you can determine whether or not it was worth the investment. With a referral system, it is easy to track your efforts and see exactly where and how everything is paying off.

Referral systems also help you save money on your advertising and marketing. Your marketing costs are reduced, but at the same time you are still obtaining a steady flow of patients. Furthermore, these patients who come to you trust you right from the start because someone referred them to you rather than their just picking an orthodontist office at random.

Initially you will need to put in some effort to make the contacts with the physicians. When they begin sending you referrals, you will feel good knowing that each time they send you one, it means they appreciate and trust the work you do. They are essentially voting with their referrals, and they are voting for your office. Not only are you strengthening the referral source each time you provide great treatment to a referral, you in turn will likely get even more referrals from the new patients themselves.

Once you get the hang of using a referral system to grow your business, you will want to keep looking for ways to hone and improve it. Creating your own system from the ground up is a fun and rewarding experience you can take pride in as you see the fruits of your labor and your patient load climb.

One of the most important things you can do for your practice is to have a referral mindset. That means you will begin looking at things differently and noticing where there may be referral opportunities. With a new mindset that is focused on helping you to work smarter rather than harder, you will find that your business grows in record time.

Not only does a referral mindset permeate your interactions with everyone you come across, but you will also begin to see that it influences other areas as well. Once you have the mindset, get your team on board, too; and you will have a practice that is destined to reach new growth goals. Your referral mindset should include the plethora of physicians who practice in your area. If you take a look around, you will probably see that it just opened up the door to a lot of new possibilities.

CHAPTER FOURTEEN

WORKING WITH REFERRING MEDICAL SPECIALISTS

WHEN YOU BEGIN TO LOOK AT YOUR COMMUNITY IN TERMS OF REFERRAL POSSIBILITIES, IT is easy to see that they are everywhere. The possibilities of who could be a potential referral source are endless. Everywhere you look, you will begin to see how your services may be of interest to another service's patients. Living with an eye for referrals is a good way to help grow your practice. It may take some practice to train your mind to think in terms of referrals, but once you do, it will be like second nature—and it will pay off.

Beyond physicians, there are plenty of other opportunities available for connecting with other medical specialists in your area. Many of them will at some point have the need to refer one of their patients to an orthodontist, and you want that referral to come to you. Whether or not that referral comes your way is largely determined by your having connected with that medical specialist or not. If they don't know your services exist, what your office is capable of, or how your charming personality is, there's a good chance someone else will get the referral.

SPEAKING THEIR LANGUAGE

After you start getting referrals from physicians, it's important to communicate with their office on the level they wish to be communicated with. Many have electronic records that will give you the opportunity to append X-rays and treatment notes directly to their care coordinators, especially if they are at a hospital. If you are not familiar with these systems, you can often take a one- to two-hour course on the weekend at the hospital as a referring specialist so you can learn the necessary skills to use the system efficiently.

It's important to speak their language. Avoid using too much dental jargon, but don't be afraid to speak in detail about exactly what you are doing to help their patient. Even though they are physicians, they may not understand the dental lingo and you don't want to leave them wondering or feeling like they need a dictionary to keep up with what's going on. Give it to them straight, but in terms they can identify with and understand so you save them time.

If you are involved in cleft care or surgical care and you haven't typically provided a lot of these services in the past, it's important to attend any multi-disciplinary meetings so you can see what other teams are doing and how you might best serve the patient and the referring physician. By doing this, you will not only learn more about working with this physician, but they will respect that you took the time to be part of it and will see you as a team member in providing treatment. Such acts will cause them to keep you in their thoughts when they have more patients who need an orthodontist referral.

Truth be told, when you first sit in on one of these meetings, you may feel a little out of place. But don't let that keep you from making the leap to do it. In my first meeting at the American Cleft Palate and Craniofacial Association, it was like landing on another planet. Surgeons, dentists, nurses, psychologists, biologists, statisticians, and social workers were all presenting on their research within their own fields, but also how it ties into team care. I honestly didn't know half of the background research they presented as common knowledge. But within a short amount of time, through immersion in this new world, I learned a great deal. I'm glad I didn't let anything keep me from becoming involved, because what I have gotten out of doing so has been extremely positive and has benefited my practice.

> *Communication is always an important component of creating a good and trustworthy relationship with a referring medical specialist.*

Communication is always an important component of creating a good and trustworthy relationship with a referring medical specialist. If they have referred a patient to you, they should never have to guess about the status of that patient being treated by you. Always keep them current on what treatment is being done and how it's progressing, and be sure to provide them with the documentation they may want to review or have for their files. They are always going to appreciate your being good with the communication, rather than them having to guess and track it down on their own.

Likewise, you will want to get any necessary information and communication from the specialist if it pertains to the treatment you are providing to the patient. The street of communication with this relationship goes both ways and must be kept open so it flows freely. When you have that open, two-way communication, you will feel like you are working well together on behalf of the patient, and you will strengthen your bond with the specialist—and you'll likely get even more future referrals.

EXPECTATIONS

When it comes down to it, you should know as much about soft tissue surgery as your surgeon knows about orthodontics. You don't have to know everything they know, obviously. But if they know what a maxillary expander is and where it attaches and what kind of expansion rate they should expect, then you should know what a Millard technique is for unilateral cleft repair or what kind of bone graft material the surgeon uses and why.

Your results in working with referring physicians are only limited to your own ability to stay curious, get outside of your box, and learn new things so you can help more people.

Keep in mind that this is an area most orthodontists overlook when it comes to seeking referrals. If you can become comfortable in seeking them out and working with the physicians, you will greatly benefit your practice. Physicians like these will have the need to work with an orthodontist. What you do now helps determine whether or not it will be your phone that rings on the day they need someone.

CHANGING HABITS

There may be some medical specialists who already have an orthodontist they refer patients to, and that's okay. You still want to make the connection with them because you never know when circumstances may change. You will also come across many doctors who do not have a set orthodontist they refer patients to. That is your golden opportunity to make a good connection and become the person they return to when they need their patient to see an orthodontist.

Many people refer to a specific person out of sheer habit. They may not even be all that impressed with the work the doctor has been doing, but providing that office name and number has simply become second nature. Making the connection with these doctors may be the little push that is needed to help get such a doctor out of that rut and to consider the idea of sending referrals your way.

Keep in mind that one of the most common reasons someone refers another person is because of their personal relationship. Referrals are largely a relationship issue, so be sure to take the time to make the connection and then try to build a relationship with the doctor. The more you can get to know the doctor and they get to know you, the more you can count on them feeling comfortable sending referrals your way.

TAKING RISKS AND DELAYING CARE

If you want to have a successful referral system in place for your practice, you have to get comfortable with the idea of taking risks. Only when you are willing to go beyond your comfort zone are you going to reach new levels with your referrals. You may not have thought before about connecting with medical specialists in your area as potential referring sources, and you may even find it a little uncomfortable to do so at first. But once you get over that initial skepticism and decide to take the risks, you will find that it pays off well.

I know plenty of orthodontists who get phone calls from potential patients but are unable to fit them in for their first appointment for months. If you have a schedule that is putting people on hold for months before they can get in to see you for the first time, there is a good chance you are delaying care too much. Referring doctors and medical specialists are not likely to appreciate that, and there's a good chance that having such a delay in the care may lead to you losing those referrals.

To provide good treatment and customer service, you need to get new patients into your office quickly. If you are putting them off for months, you need to make some changes; and these changes may involve you taking some risks. But again, taking risks can lead to some beneficial outcomes, so don't be afraid to take them.

Perhaps you need to find additional hours to be open, or consider hiring another orthodontist to work for you in your office. These are going to prove to be more lucrative options than pushing people off, because when care is delayed, there is a good chance you will lose those patients, especially ones who are being referred by specialists. The specialists are likely looking to have treatment begin promptly for their patients.

MAINTAINING REFERRAL SOURCES

It's important that you take the steps to get this type of referral source in your community. Take a look around, and you are bound to see plenty of medical specialists, with each of them needing an orthodontist to refer people to at least once in a while. You want to be that person they think of, and you will be if you make it a priority to put yourself out there and make some connections with these people. Until you do that, they don't know about you; you're just one of numerous others in your area. Take the necessary steps to put yourself out there and stand out to each of these people.

Once you begin to obtain these referral sources, your next step is to focus on keeping them. The best way to do that is to treat their patients well and provide great treatment. As you are providing treatment for their patient, always maintain an open line of communication with the referring medical specialist so they know what's going on and where the treatment is along the spectrum. You should strive to keep both the patient and the specialist who referred them to you happy.

It's important that you always take the time to thank them for their referral, keep in regular contact with them, meet in person when it's possible, and give them a plug here and there when you can. Staying in contact and meeting them when possible is the foundation for building a relationship which is going to sustain the referral source for years to come. If you have a blog, newsletter, or Facebook page, you may want to give them a shout out once in a while to get their name out there. They will appreciate that you are doing something in return for them so it's not always just a one-way street of referrals going to your office.

Keep in mind that one of the most common reasons someone refers another person is because of their personal relationship.

One thing that should be avoided once a referral relationship has been established is for the referral source to only hear from you when they refer someone to your office. Ideally, that relationship should be active outside of those referrals. Maintain communication of some sort with that referral source, even if it has been a while since they have sent a referral your way. This keeps you on their mind so that your name is what they think of the next time they need to refer a patient. Plus, it helps strengthen the relationship you have with that specialist, which should increase your chances of getting referrals from them.

CONSIDERING ALL ANGLES

I have worked with many other orthodontists over the years, providing consultation and insight about what makes my system work so well. I've also listened as they tell me what their referral system is like, or the many reasons why they may not have one in place at all. I've even heard stories of other orthodontists who focused on getting one specific doctor to send them referrals, but forgot the need to cast their net wider. They went years getting a steady supply of referrals from the doctor and assumed that's all they needed to do. Then one day, something happened—perhaps for a reason, or for no reason at all—and the referrals stopped.

When that type of thing happens, orthodontists suddenly realize why it's not such a good idea to have all of their referral eggs in one basket, so to speak. If that one doctor or referral source dries up and stops sending you referrals—for whatever reason—your steady stream of patients will dry up, too. It can happen to anyone, even if you think the relationship is strong and a sure source for continuous referrals.

There are many reasons why a referral source could dry up, and some of them may have nothing to do with you or your service. You could be doing everything right and still find out that a referring doctor or specialist has begun sending their referrals to another orthodontist. Despite your best efforts, this can still happen sometimes. Office staff changes, and employee turnover can lead to a shift in where referrals are sent.

Having a successful referral system includes casting a wide net. You want to consider every possible route to receiving referrals.

A referring doctor or specialist will likely not contact you to explain the reason why they aren't sending you referrals any longer. Knowing the reason might help you make some beneficial changes to your practice, but the switch in who they refer to may actually have nothing to do with you. If that is the case, you most likely didn't establish much of a relationship with that source in the first place.

The bottom line is that you are not likely to find out why those referrals stopped coming—unless they are no longer in business—because the doctor or office manager is not going to want to have a confrontation with you. It's easier just to make the switch and start giving your referrals to someone else than it is for them to confront you with what you did to lose their trust and referrals—if that's why they stopped. Don't take it personally or let it slow you down. Turn your focus to those who do still refer people to you and from whom you can obtain even more new referrals.

One of the most important messages I share with those I work with is that they must diversify their referral sources. Having one source that brings you a steady supply of referrals is great. It's wonderful. But it cannot be your *only* source, or there is a good chance you may be in trouble at some point. The fewer referral sources you have at your disposal, the higher your risk of not getting what you need to survive and thrive.

Having a successful referral system includes casting a wide net. You want to consider every possible route to receiving referrals. That's why we don't just stop at getting patients to refer their friends or getting one dentist to send us their referrals. When you dig deeper and cast your net wider, you will see that there are many more options beyond those two. It's all about changing your mindset so you can begin to see doctors and medical specialists as potential referral sources. The wider you cast your net, the higher your chances that you will get more referrals to grow your practice. You will also be creating more security for your practice, because the referrals will be coming from numerous sources.

There are always going to be risks involved when you establish relationships with referral sources, but you can minimize them. Keep networking and reaching out to other sources on a regular basis. You may even want to set a goal for how many new contacts you will make each month that are possible referral sources. Always stay in touch with both your patients and your referring sources. Keeping the connection there is important, regardless of whether it is one of your patients or a dentist from across town.

Having a back-up system or source in place is just smart business. It assures that no matter what happens to one particular place in town, your office will still thrive, and you will still continue to get referrals from your multiple other sources. Maintaining a back-up system may seem more difficult than it really is; but once you get everything going, it will seem like second nature and can only work to your advantage. After a while, no doubt you will have the referral mindset you need to propel your practice to reach new levels.

HONING YOUR SKILLS

As you work with area physicians and medical specialists, you may have the need to give presentations. These can be great tools for bringing in these professionals and laying the foundation for a relationship or personal connection. Host a seminar or give a talk on a specific topic these doctors and specialists would be interested in. A lot of good information is readily available that will help you pull off a great presentation. In the end, you will lay the foundation for new relationships by making contact with each person who attended.

Your practice may still end up engaging in marketing even though you have a referral system in place, but there are many things you can do to get more referrals out of the places you already get referrals from. Your existing referral sources are great when you want to increase the number of referrals coming your way each month. For starters, it is important for your referral system to be in place. It can no longer just be a thought or idea you haven't yet started. Once you get the referral system started, you will then need to work at keeping it going. This may require you to schedule some time each week that is dedicated to your referral system. Having a set referral system in place with a plan of how you will maintain it is going to assure you the best possible way to keep a steady flow of referrals coming into your office.

Medical specialists will send you referrals when they trust you. After all, each time they send one of their patients your way, they are putting their own reputation on the line. They need to know you are going to provide their patient with quality care. Once they trust you, they will send you more patients on a regular basis. To build trust, you have to establish a relationship with people.

I've had plenty of orthodontists tell me that when they try to build these relationships, they feel like they are salespeople, rather than doctors who are trying to gain referrals. If that's what it feels like, then you don't have the right focus. Relationships with these professionals in your community will take time and patience in order for them to grow and for them to begin trusting you with their patients. Your job in making the connection with them is not to sell them on something and make a financial transaction. Instead, your mission is to find out how you can help fill their needs. When you make it more about what you can do to help them rather than about selling yourself, you will find you have greater success.

PRIORITIZING YOUR REFERRAL SOURCES

Once you have your referral system in place, you will soon discover that each referral source can be placed on a spectrum from the highest to lowest possible number of referrals. It's a good idea to prioritize your referrals so you can get the most out of those who can send you the most. Identify which referral sources have the potential to send you the most people and prioritize those at the top. Keep in mind that each level in your prioritization matters and collectively will bring in many people, so each level will need special attention devoted to cultivating a relationship. However, those who are at the high end of the spectrum are more likely to be your most lucrative source for bringing in new referrals, so you want to treat them extra special throughout the year and do your best to remain on their radar in a professional and caring way, without being overbearing or annoying.

When you have identified who your largest potential source of referrals may be, you can maximize your efforts in building a relationship with that person or office. Those referral sources at the lower end of the spectrum are likely ones that don't yet know all you are able to do for them, or perhaps they are not in as close proximity as you would like. They can still become valuable referral sources, but it will take time to build the relationship for that to happen. The majority of the time you put into your referral system upkeep should go to those at the top of your priority list, those sources which have the greatest potential for a high number of referrals. But you should still dedicate some time each month to those at the bottom of your list as well.

> *Relationships with these professionals in your community will take time and patience in order for them to grow and for them to begin trusting you with their patients.*

Keep in mind that you should probably reprioritize your referral source list once or twice per year. There are shifts that may take place which you need to account for. Doctors and specialists may move, or you will have a referral source who has moved up the priority list. By keeping track of the source of all your referrals, you can easily access that information and use it to reprioritize your referral list. This will help you determine where the bulk of your referral system maintenance time should be going.

PROTECTING RELATIONSHIPS

Over the years, I have heard from many orthodontists who let good referral sources slip through their hands. They took them for granted and reduced the amount of relationship building and maintaining they had always been doing before. Next thing they knew, that referral source took a turn and began sending their referrals elsewhere.

Don't assume you have a particular referral source locked in and therefore don't have to work on the relationship with that person or office. That's completely the opposite of reality. That relationship may be going well, but you should never take that source for granted.

Once you take a referral source for granted, you begin to lose what brought you those referrals in the first place. You will no longer appreciate their referrals, give them a proper thank-you, or try to strengthen the relationship you have with them. People who take their referral source for granted assume it's locked in and there is nothing else they need to do to keep the relationship going.

If you've neglected a relationship and the referrals dry up, you shouldn't call the office to let them know you noticed they haven't sent a referral your way in a while, because by that time, it will make it appear as though you only care about the referrals drying up, rather than in maintaining a relationship all along. You are not going to hear complaints from them if something is going wrong. More likely than not, the referrals will stop coming from that particular doctor without any notice or indication as to why. There's a good chance you will never find out the real reason why your referrals from a particular place stopped coming your way, even if you are able to ask someone in that office about the issue.

> If you take your referral sources for granted, you have a much higher risk that your competition will be successful in taking the referrals away from you.

Always be aware of the fact that there are other orthodontists who are out to take your referral sources. You may not see them in action or even know exactly which ones it may be. But make no mistake, they are there. They are reaching out to those doctors and medical specialists, and they are making a case for referring to their practice over yours. They are taking the time to try and connect with those sources and build a relationship with them. Some will succeed in doing so; others will not.

If you take your referral sources for granted, you have a much higher risk that your competition will be successful in taking the referrals away from you. If you make taking care of your referral system a priority and work on maintaining it each week, you can keep this from happening. Your current sources will not feel taken for granted, so they will be more likely to remain loyal to your office; and you will be strengthening the relationships as well. Don't wait until you lose a referral source before you sit up, take notice, and begin to take action. By then it's usually too late because they have moved on to sending their patients to someone else. In all likelihood, if you have already lost the referrals, you will have a difficult time getting them back.

Make the relationship a priority from the start, and always work at maintaining it, even if you have to put it on your calendar as a task so you don't forget to do it.

Do what it takes to keep the relationship growing and strengthening.

Not only do you want to work on your offense when it comes to your referral system, but you also need to work on your defense. You worked hard to get the referrals you have—or that you will soon have—so you also want to play some defense to keep them. It's much easier to keep your current referral sources than it is to keep going out and getting new ones. Your best assets when it comes to your referrals are the ones you currently have, especially those who are at the top of your referral priority list.

REMEMBER THE STAFF

A couple years back, I was consulting an orthodontist who told me that they did everything right when it came to getting referrals from a particular medical specialist. They communicated with that doctor, sent thank-you messages for referrals, and even stopped by once every other month to see them personally and strengthen the relationship. Yet after about a year of this, the specialist began sending referrals to another orthodontist down the road. Having no clue as to why this happened *Never underestimate the importance of those who work in that doctor's or specialist's office.* to him, I began to probe deeper to find out what could have happened or gone wrong. I asked questions, listened carefully to his answers, and then asked more based on his responses.

What I found out during that discussion is that although he spent a great deal of effort to make a positive impression on the referring doctor, he simply didn't get along well with the office manager. She was often the one who would be there when he stopped by to see the doctor, but he paid her no attention at all. In fact, he had gotten into a bit of a disagreement with her once about a minor issue—well, it at least seemed minor to him, but it was one more thing about him that made her not like him. He seriously underestimated the value of getting along with the staff at each referring office.

Never underestimate the importance of those who work in that doctor's or specialist's office. They are often the front line when it comes to patients calling and asking for referrals or additional information. Plus, even though this particular doctor took the time to do everything right in building a relationship with this referring source, he overlooked a crucial part of the equation. Had he taken the time to give even a little effort to building a relationship with the office manager, there is a good chance he'd still be getting those referrals. In the end, the decision about whether or not referrals will be sent your way won't fall completely on the shoulders of the doctor or specialist. He or she is going to take into account how their office staff feels, too.

If you're overlooking those greeting you at the front desk or answering your calls there, then you are demonstrating that you only care about the referrals and not about people in general. Always, always, always be pleasant to those who work in the offices. Their opinion often carries a lot of weight when it comes to making recommendations and referring people, especially if they have the opportunity to throw their own personal opinion in there for good measure.

From what I could gather, this particular orthodontist didn't take the time to build a relationship with the office manager, much to his detriment. In fact, it wasn't just that he didn't build a relationship; his lack of trying to connect at all ended up working against him. In all likelihood, she spoke to the doctor about it, possibly even suggesting an alternative for where to send referrals; and the doctor listened.

The lesson here is that all relationships count, whether it's with the doctor or medical specialist, or those who work in their office. You never know who has what influence, and those relationship opportunities should never be overlooked.

WORKING WITH OTHER SMALL BUSINESS OWNERS, MEDICAL SPAS, HEALTH FAIRS, AND COMMUNITY EVENTS

MY GUESS IS THAT THE VAST MAJORITY OF ORTHODONTISTS ARE NOT AWARE OF THE potential there is in working with other small business owners, medical spas, health fairs, and community events. Meanwhile, this has been a tremendous referral source for our practices over the years and the one many other orthodontists shy away from. Most steer clear of trying to get referrals from other businesses out of fear of being tacky, pushy, salesy, or any other excuse they can think of that will allow them to sit on their duffs and not get out into the world and build relationships.

KNOWING YOUR NEIGHBORS

You may be surprised at just how many referral opportunities are surrounding your office right now in the form of other businesses and community events. If you have a famous steak restaurant right across the parking lot from your office, for example, have you gone over there to talk about doing your holiday party there, how you can offer their employees a discount on Invisalign or whitening? How you can sponsor the little matchbooks, mints, and toothpicks they hand out? Or how you might even get on the back of the survey card that comes out with every bill? Then you are undoubtedly leaving money and referrals on the table.

How long do you want to continue to leave that money on the table? Opportunities to gain new referral sources are all around you. Do you have a popular coffee shop near your practice? Have you ever asked them if you can put your logo and coupon on the little coffee sleeves they pass out? (You would buy the sleeves and have them printed, so you're covering one of their overhead expenses.) How about giving your patients a free treat on their birthday via a coupon to the coffee store for a buy-one, get-one smoothie? This would especially be a win-win for all parties because the coupon is essentially a free gift from you to your patients (there's no cost to you), your patients get a free smoothie, and the coffee shop gets a free customer since customers have to buy one to get one. Everyone wins.

If you haven't done something like this, then again I say you are leaving money and referrals on the table. Take another look around the area near your practice, and you may find you have an elementary or middle school right across the road or down the block. If you aren't the key sponsor on the scoreboard in the gym, you're not on the back of every school program, and you're not handing out free seat cushions on the home opener of every sport season ("Brace Yourself for a Great Season!" courtesy of Smith Orthodontics), then you are again leaving money and referrals on the table.

The opportunities for tapping into referral sources from businesses are all around you. Perhaps you haven't noticed them before as you drive by, walk by, and even grab your lunch there, but they exist. They exist in a major way, and hopefully after reading this chapter you will begin looking at these places in a different way. It all comes down to finding an angle to get your name in the business somewhere so that their customers are exposed to your office.

For smart business owners who really get this concept, you can offer to do an endorsed letter. That's where you write a letter in the other business owner's voice, you have the owner approve it, and then send it with their signature on their letterhead in an envelope so that it looks like it came from their business. The letter, addressed to the business's customers, could include information like this:

> *"As a patron of our fine business and someone who appreciates the highest quality, I've discovered from my friends at Smith Orthodontics that they have the same high standards of quality. So high, in fact, that my wife and I are being treated there, and I think you might enjoy meeting them as well. When you tell them that Dan from Dan's Steakhouse sent you, they have a special new patient welcome packet and gift waiting for you as a special courtesy only to the fine customers at my restaurants. Sincerely, Dan"*

When you get know your business neighbors well, you will discover that they open up a whole new world of referral source opportunities for your practice. Another good thing about this is that there are so many of them around. In all likelihood, your practice is surrounded by businesses, all of which are potential referral sources for your practice. Don't wait for them to reach out to you for the lines of communication to open. Take the initiative to put the wheels in motion and begin communicating with them.

MEETING NEEDS

Most businesses in your area that you connect with are not going to accept you with open arms, willing and eager for you to get in touch with their customer base. It would be naïve of us to believe this would be so. But that doesn't mean they won't warm up quickly to the idea of reaching out to their customers. It's all in the approach that you take and what you do that is going to determine whether or not you get the opportunity in the first place.

Every business around you has a need you can help them with. When you determine what that need is, you will have the edge to get your practice in front of their customers. Consider each business carefully to determine what you can do for them. What need can you fill that will warm them up to the idea of your reaching their customer base? Perhaps you want to focus on just building a relationship with the business owner as you take your business to them. Whether it's a coffee shop or a printing company, you likely have needs of your own that they can help meet. By going to them for those particular needs, you will form a relationship; and once that begins to grow, there is a good chance they will be open to the idea of working with you to get your practice name out there to their customers.

Every business around you has a need you can help them with. When you determine what that need is, you will have the edge to get your practice in front of their customers.

When working with these surrounding businesses, you want to get creative in your thinking. If you have a nearby café, see if you can have an ad on their paper placemats. Nearby schools are great places to advertise as well. They are often cash-strapped, and this alone will give you some opportunities for getting your name into the school. You can speak with the health professional to discuss setting up free screenings, or providing every student in the school with a new toothbrush. Along with that toothbrush, the kids will receive your informational card and possibly a special offer. At many schools you can also work with the PTA in order to get your name out there to the parents. The

PTAs today are often on fundraising missions, so for reasonable fees, you may be able to have your practice advertised on a banner at the school, or for a small fee have an informational flier sent home with each student. They may also offer reasonable online advertising options that are seen by a good portion of the parents whose children attend the school.

There are plenty of ways to tap into the power all local businesses and organizations can offer your referral system. It takes you having a plan and sticking with it to connect with these various places. You don't need to contact them all in the same week of course, but you should make a goal to contact at least one new place every week and see what you can do. By working with these area businesses, you will have an edge that other orthodontists in your area likely don't have. Most never think to work with such companies, leaving them all available to you.

THE LADDER

When you work with the businesses in your area, it pays to know their chain of command. You will want to speak with the business's manager, owner, or decision makers. Those are the people who are going to get you the information you need and will make the decisions about what you can and can't to do to help them out—and ultimately to get in front of their customers. While you want to build a good reputation with everyone you come across, you especially want to focus on building relationships with those at the top. Businesses often have high turnover rates, so the person running the register or taking orders today may not be the same person doing it a week or month from now.

Keep in mind, too, that there is usually a gatekeeper at many businesses. Sometimes the person is the receptionist, who has been taught to keep calls and visitors from getting through to the manager or owner. They get many people throughout the week who try to make their acquaintance, so they train these gatekeepers to be selective about who they let through. Don't be upset with the gatekeepers as they try to keep you from getting to their boss. They are merely doing their job. Be nice to them and keep trying without being overly pushy. There is a good chance you will eventually get through, especially if you have made a connection with the gatekeeper or receptionist. If that person likes you, they are more likely to put in a good word for you and get your message passed up to the next level.

When approaching the businesses in your area, find out who the manager or owner is and when that person is available. Stop back by when they are working so you can meet face-to-face and lay the foundation for a relationship. Keep in mind that you want to be kind to everyone you come across in these businesses because you never know which ones may speak to people about your practice or what type of influence that person has on the decision-making of that business. Besides, being kind to people you meet should go without saying. It's something you should be doing everywhere and anywhere.

A good way to effectively collaborate with other local businesses is to join your Chamber of Commerce. If you have a good one, as many places do, you will have the opportunity to build relationships with numerous businesses in your community. These organizations often hold member events featuring breakfasts, guest speakers, ribbon cuttings, and more. Each of these events is open to all Chamber members, and they give you an opportunity to meet with people from other businesses. You would be surprised at the relationships you can build with others in your area just by joining the group and attending some of their events. If you can't personally attend, perhaps you can have someone from your office dedicated to doing so. Either way, having a presence there is a good thing because it takes the pressure off, you won't feel like you are selling yourself, and you will have the chance to chat with these people and work on relationship building, which is the foundation of giving and receiving referrals.

If you don't have an active Chamber group in your area, log onto meetup. com to see what local business groups you have that are active. You may find there are local chapters of business groups in your area, or other types of groups that make sense for you to connect with in order to meet those other business owners. While you are exploring meetup.com, see what other types of groups are in your area. Now that you are thinking more with the referral mindset, determine which groups would make sense for you to meet up with and try to connect with them.

BUSINESS COLLABORATION

When it comes to collaborating with the businesses in your area, you need to get creative. I'm a firm believer that there is something you could do with each and every business out there in order to collaborate, but you have to get really creative in determining how that may be achieved. Working with other businesses in your area will strengthen the feeling of community and will give each of you the ability to help each other.

There are plenty of opportunities for collaborating, depending on the type of business you are teaming up with. Consider the options that exist for having signage and informational brochures in each other's business, offering discounts to each other's customers, and more. There are even more opportunities when it comes to sponsorships, cross-promoting events, coupons, and special offers.

Not every type of opportunity for collaboration will make sense to each business out there. This is where you have to get creative. Your job is to go in already armed with a few ideas about what you can do to work together. Consider which ideas make sense for that particular type of business, keeping in mind that not every idea will be a good fit for each type of business. Make the suggestions and see where they lead to. Perhaps the person you are collaborating with will also have some suggestions, including ones you haven't yet thought of. They may be better ideas, or they may simply be more acceptable to that business manager. Be open-minded to the ideas and go from there to determine the course of action you want to take to work together.

What you are doing with the other businesses is not set in stone. It can always be changed and you can both take a different direction at any time.

The important thing is to get started in the first place. That way you can see what works and what needs to be altered in order to be more effective. It's important to always be honest, realistic, and reliable with the people you are working with in these businesses. Share your story and be sure to talk benefits. People need to know what the benefits are for them and their customers. Above all, make it more about building a relationship with that business than about earning money from what they can do for you. If you care about the relationship and focus on building and fostering it, everything else will fall into place, including the referrals to your office and an increase in revenue.

Working with other businesses in your area will strengthen the feeling of community and will give each of you the ability to help each other.

Businesses can always benefit from providing their customers with added value. If you can find a way to help them do that and get your name out there at the same time—possibly along with a special offer—then it will be a win-win situation for both of you. It can be done, and it can be done effectively in order to increase the number of referrals you get to your practice.

When it comes to businesses working together, I like to remind myself of this quote by Henry Ford: "If everyone is moving forward together, then success takes care of itself."

MEDICAL SPAS

There are many different types of medical spas around the country, with more opening their doors all the time. Consider the variety of options they offer; they specialize in such things as aesthetic medicine, dermatology, anti-aging medicine, cosmetic surgery, acupuncture, chiropractic care, massage, and more. They run the gamut on the types of medical specialists they employ and the services they provide. They are also ideal places to collaborate with when you are building an effective referral system.

Most people who visit medical spas do so because they are interested in corrective care. Whether it be Botox injections to minimize their wrinkles, or they want to reduce the appearance of stretch marks, there is a good chance they are seeking treatment to enhance their appearance. The medical spas can't provide the services that an orthodontist does, but they can direct their patients where to get them.

Seek out the medical spas in your area and put them on your list of places to get to know. See what you can do to team up with them or exchange promotions and referrals. There are plenty of opportunities to explore, including supplying them with discount offers and brochures, plugging them on Facebook, linking to their site for recommended medical professionals, or teaming up with them to host an event.

HEALTH FAIRS

Most cities offer some type of health fair throughout the year. They may be held at the health department, in a mall, or along a busy, trendy street where people can stroll by at their leisure. Regardless of how they are set up, health fairs exist for one purpose: to get health information out to the public. This is a great opportunity for you to get your practice's information out to the people in your community as well.

There are numerous ways to get involved with health fairs. Businesses are typically allowed to set up a booth, so set one up for your practice. At the booth, you can hand out information, create some fun games, and answer questions. It's a great opportunity to network with others and meet people in the community. If you can't attend the health fair personally, it's a good idea to send someone from your office who knows what the mission is and will carry it out on your behalf. The goal is to get your info out to the community, make connections with a lot of people, and lay the foundation for referrals to be coming in once the health fair is over.

Other options for getting involved in health fairs include being one of the sponsors of the event so that your office gets more exposure when it is promoted and by sending home a discount offer in the goodie bags. Many health fairs, and even races, provide gift bags to those who attend or participate. Having an offer or helpful pamphlet printed up and added to the bag to go home with everyone is an inexpensive way to get your name out. It's also a targeted market because the people who attend are already seeking health information.

Keep an eye out for upcoming health events in your area so you can see how your practice can get involved. They often happen around particular times of the year, such as spring and February (which is American Heart Month). Contact your health department to inquire about any upcoming health fairs so you can get them on your calendar. If they have none planned, this may be the ideal time to suggest they do so. If they know the interest is there for medical professionals in the community, they are more likely to put the wheels in motion to get one planned. Health fairs also take place at schools and medical facilities, so inquire about any that may be on the horizon at your local hospitals.

COMMUNITY EVENTS

The number of opportunities that exist for you to get involved with community events is endless. In most cities, they seem to take place all year long. Consider all of the different types of events you've likely seen on a regular basis in your area: marathons and races, fairs, parades, food truck bazaars, outdoor movies, spring and summer camp fairs, art strolls, and more. There is a good chance dozens of events are taking place in your community on a regular basis.

Every one of those community events is an opportunity for you to get involved in some capacity. Perhaps your practice doesn't seem like a good fit for all of the events, and that's fine. You don't have to sponsor or participate in all of them. Find the ones that do make sense for you to get involved in. For example, a kids' back-to-school fair is a great opportunity for you to get your name in front of families. One event may simply be a better fit for you practice than the other. Both events, however, are likely to give you some exposure that will lead to referrals coming your way. At the same time, targeting the ones that are a better fit will end up yielding better returns.

Community events put on by others may be happening in your area all year long, but they are not the only options you have. Organizing your own community events is an effective method we use to reach out to people all throughout the year. We plan events that the public is invited to, such as outdoor movie screenings and fun events for families. These events are free, held at or near the office, and give people a chance to learn more about our practice.

By hosting a free outdoor movie, complete with free popcorn and other snacks, you will stand out and end up on the radar of some of the people who attend. If you host an event like this, get the word out and make sure people realize it's free and open to the public. Promote it to your current patients, too, and tell them to bring a friend for the fun and festivities. Have a drawing for prizes, walk around and talk to people, and make it a great time for everyone.

If you're organizing community events, keep in mind that they don't have to be only for the public, such as hosting a kid's dental health month party. You can also host some events that are for other professionals or entrepreneurs in your area. Hosting these networking events and inviting specific groups of people in your community will open up new doors and bring in a wide variety of people you can meet and who can learn about your services. Whether you are offering continuing education events, sponsoring a 5K brace race, or inviting all of your patients to attend a barbecue, the number of opportunities is endless.

Organizing your own community events is an effective method to reach out to people all throughout the year.

Any events you will be hosting need to be properly promoted in order for your efforts to be effective. Make sure everything is well organized and planned out, and be sure to know what you want to get out of the event. If you have an objective, you will be able to measure it and know if your efforts were successful or not.

To promote your events, be sure to send out professional information across all channels. You should send out a press release, post about it on your social media, include it in your newsletter and on your website, and post information about it in your office. It's also a good idea to send event details to any bloggers in your area who cover community events or health-related information.

When planning your own events, keep in mind you can entice more people to attend if you give away prizes. Have a drawing for some free gifts, such as an iPad mini or local restaurant gift certificates. You may even be able to collaborate with other local businesses to get them to supply the restaurant gift cards or other items which will be randomly given away in exchange for saying that the prize was graciously donated by that company. The same goes for you having the ability to offer gifts to be given away when others are hosting events. Collaboration is always a good thing to consider and may be helpful in creating great events.

Once people attend your event, you want to let them see you having fun and being personable. Talk to as many people as you can. Every time you do that, you are building a relationship with that person which will increase your chances of getting referrals. Take pictures of people having fun at the event, and be sure to post them on your social media so those people can share them, thus increasing the likelihood of your getting referrals from their friends and family. Capture names and email addresses with your CRM software and notify raffle winners. Then, follow-up with new patient offers and specials.

SMALL BUSINESS NETWORKING

There has been a movement across the nation for people to support their local small businesses. People generally feel good supporting small businesses, and you can use that angle to work with other small businesses in your area. When you collaborate with them and you all support each other, people will appreciate it and will be further encouraged to support those local businesses.

There are many ways that a small business networking group can come together to reach the public. While you may host some of the community events, others can take turns hosting some as well. By networking, you can all gain the benefits of having a presence at the event, but they won't all have to be put on by the same business each time. This should bring in different people to the events, helping you all to cast your net wider and reach more referral sources.

Some of the event opportunities that you will want to put on your calendar and do something for each year include the following. Most orthodontists only think in terms of events like October and National Orthodontic Health Month. Unfortunately, every orthodontist in your area will be hosting events in October for National Orthodontic Health Month. Instead of blending in with every other orthodontist, do something that stands out throughout the year. Additional event opportunities include the following:

JANUARY
New Year's Day (focus a campaign on resolutions)

FEBRUARY
National Pet Dental Health Month (team up with a local veterinarian)
American Heart Month (focus on heart health and oral care connection)
National Children's Dental Health Month (host a Braces 101 or other such event to provide information on braces and other services)

MARCH

National Nutrition Month (look for health fairs and offer tips on eating for healthy teeth and safe foods for braces)

APRIL

World Health Day (look for local health fairs and community health events)
National Youth Sports Safety Month (team up with local youth sports teams to provide information on oral safety)

JUNE

Professional Wellness Month (reach out to professional offices in your area to provide information on services, offer a braces for adults luncheon)

JULY

National Ice Cream Month and National Hot Dog Month (hold an ice cream social for the community, give away free hot dogs at an outdoor movie event)

OCTOBER

Child Health Day, held every October 1st (contact schools about providing health information that can be sent home to parents, or give a talk to classrooms)
National Dental Hygiene Month (focus on schools and teaming up with dentists to have a community event)

NOVEMBER

Small Business Saturday, held the day after Black Friday (team up with local small businesses)

These are just a sampling of the options that exist. Each of these is an opportunity to host an event yourself that is open to your patients and the community, or it's a chance to team up with those in your area to host such events. You may also find that someone in your community is already planning some of these events, making it easier for you to get in on the action. Whether sponsoring it, setting up a booth, or finding another way to network and reach out to people, you will find that you will get a good return on your investment by getting involved.

Another good option to consider when it comes to community events is getting involved in parades. Families love parades, and parades tend to bring communities together for an afternoon of fun. You can put your practice in the parade by having a float that is decked out with some braces and looks fun.

Pass out candy to the kids and information to the adults. With as many hands as you will get the information into, you are bound to get some referrals from your efforts. Plus, being a part of the parade demonstrates your fun side and that you support community events. People will like seeing that about you and will become more interested. If you are in it yourself, you will even get a chance to meet some new people, network, and put on a fun face for the afternoon.

There are plenty of opportunities available for the person who is eager to make connections with those in the community. Sure, you can't do them all; but you should carve out some time each year to get involved in some. The community will appreciate it and your efforts will pay off in helping to strengthen your referral system.

SHYING AWAY

Throughout my consulting and speaking engagements over the years, I have met many orthodontists. Among them, there have been quite a few who have told me they are not comfortable with reaching out to others. They don't care about networking, hosting events, or taking part in community activities. They know that I'm a big fan of these approaches and have used them in my own practice in order to build an incredible referral system. Yet they still shy away from such things and feel that it is being too much like a salesperson—and they didn't sign up for that when they became an orthodontist.

I understand where the mentality comes from. I really do. But if this describes you, then I'm urging you to break through that uncomfortable shell and get yourself acclimated to the new waters. You may be the best damned orthodontist within a 100-mile radius, but without people knowing about your office, that fact won't help your practice grow. You have to be your number one driving force in bringing referrals into your practice, and you do that by creating an awesome referral system.

It's not being pushy to want to share what you do with others around you. Like others in the field, you likely went into the field to help people. Now you need to let them know you exist and what you can do for them. Never apologize for letting people know you have the skills and experience to meet their need. It's nothing to feel bad about or shy away from. Like Jack Canfield says, "Everything you want is on the other side of fear."

CHAPTER SIXTEEN

THE BIG EVENT—
HOW TO USE EVENTS
FOR MORE REFERRALS

BY NOW YOU'VE PROBABLY REALIZED THAT IF YOU WANT TO BE IN THE REFERRAL BUSINESS, you must get into the event business. Why events? They are the quickest, most-powerful way to get people excited and talking about you. If you look at the recording and entertainment industries today, one of the largest profit centers is live events. World tours and back-to-back, sold-out events are the quickest way to generate buzz, word-of-mouth, and sales.

You must give your customers a reason to talk about you and drag their referrals directly to you—preferably in great big droves. One of the most successful ways our businesses and the businesses of my coaching clients have generated a flood of new customers is through exclusive events. But don't take my word for it; there are a host of massively successful companies using events to drive new customers through the door year after year. Some you will recognize, others you will not. All of them have powerful lessons for serious students willing to learn from this chapter.

Before we get started with the lessons, let's recap what most small business owners think about referrals and the strategies I see most of these businesses take when it comes to generating more word-of-mouth business. Ask yourself as you read this chapter, "How often am I confused regarding the truth about referrals and what it takes to generate more word-of-mouth business?" Write down your answers. This is not an academic exercise; the strategies presented here and throughout this book will grow your business. You decide how and when you want to implement them.

REFERRAL STRATEGIES FOR THE AVERAGE BUSINESS

1. Hope.
2. Pray.
3. Do nothing.
4. Bitch and moan about the results.

There is virtually no limit to the types of events you can organize to generate referrals, from small intimate gatherings of your best referrers, a spa day or an exclusive fly fishing trip, to large record-breaking events with live music, free food, and impressive attractions. In this chapter you will learn the main principles of running events to generate more referrals. Although these principles apply to events of all shapes and sizes, after reading each example, you will want to take notes on specific implementation ideas and consider the resources you would need and parameters you must set to create your own successful event.

Rule #1: Invite the Right People

Last time I checked, you can't have an event without people, so you might as well invite the right ones.

First, make a list of every influential customer in your business. Start with those who have referred patients to you in the past and those you feel have great potential to refer if given the right opportunity to do so.

Next, look up the customers who have spent the most money with you in the last year. Our data show that our highest spenders are more likely to refer by a 3:1 margin.

Third, pull together a list of customers who have purchased one of your books, have left a favorable online review, or who own a small business. These individuals are typically in tune with your marketing message and love to see what you're up to. They are, as Ken Blanchard says, your "raving fans." Be sure to invite them.

Finally, generate a list of customers who were referred by another customer. Although these people are not a sure-fire bet to refer another friend or family member, with the right message and appropriate invitation, you can remind them that they discovered your business through one of their friends or family, and then invite them to "share the love."

Accurate thinking about your event and who gets invited are more than an exercise in list segmentation. Your event is designed to generate more referrals.

The joke in my office is that we don't do these events for our health. We do them to generate new word-of-mouth business. If you invite the customers who heard about you from a discount offer or because you were the most convenient or cheapest provider of a product or service, you will create an event that is loved by all and acted on by none. You want results from your event. Be sure to invite the right people.

Rule #2: Make It Exclusive

This principle is complementary to and plays hand-in-hand with the first rule. By asking you to segment your list and invite the people who are most likely to refer their friends and family, I have effectively "tricked" you into creating an exclusive event.

Years ago, growing up in Ohio, I quickly discovered in my grandfather's auto part store that you don't leave money on the table. If we had an auto part in stock that no one else in town had and we failed to point that out to the customer, we were promptly reminded that we just left money on the table. Imagine a customer driving around town to three or four auto parts stores and only one store had the needed part in stock. With a simple sales message, another product or service could be *If something is exclusive and you don't promote it as exclusive, you are leaving money on the table.* quickly sold by reminding the customer, "By the time the other stores in town even get this part in stock, we can have it installed in your car and get you back on the road today. Do you want us to go ahead and get this done while you are here or would you prefer to drop the car off later tonight?"

By segmenting your list into those customers who are more likely to refer versus those customers who are more likely to enjoy your free event without referring anyone, you have created an exclusive event. Now go out there and remind your best customers that this event is for your best referrers only. It does not matter if the event is designed for only 10 people or over 500. The only difference that matters is the heightened level at which you can play the exclusivity card. For an event with 500 customers, you could and should mention that this event is for your top customers only.

However, for an event designed with your top 10 referrers in mind, you should play the exclusivity card to the highest extent. All of your top referrers should know they are in the running for an exclusive event like a wine dinner, day of shopping, or extravagant spa experience. It should be clearly stated that you can only take 10 people. You would be a fool not to mention that this opportunity is highly exclusive. You know you're getting it right when people call and are dying to know when your next spa day is just in case they cannot make it to the one you've advertised.

Rule #3: Give Them Bragging Rights

In the world of business, Warren Buffett is a name you should know well. His investing prowess has landed him in the ranks of the world's wealthiest people, with a net worth of $72.3 billion as of this writing. As the most successful investor of the twentieth century, Buffett has done more than a few things right. A single share of his holding company, Berkshire Hathaway, has currently returned an astounding 2,850,000 percent since Buffett began buying up shares in the 1980s. In 2012, a charity auction of spending a few hours at lunch with Buffett with no questions off the table netted a record $3.5 million bid. Clearly, he has no problem attracting investors and high net worth individuals who want to learn from him. His company welcomes over 40,000 people to Omaha each year for their shareholder event alone.

Simply hiring an emcee who is adored by the community, like the local news anchor or meteorologist, makes fine fodder for Facebook and Twitter posts. Ignore this principle at your event's peril.

Like many shareholder events, there is a presentation of results from the previous year and predictions for the upcoming year. There are meetings and lunches and votes that must take place. What separates Buffett's annual event from anything else like it is the unmistakable excitement and brag-worthiness of coming back home and telling your investor friends what you just did or learned at the Berkshire Hathaway meeting in Omaha last weekend. Buffett rides into the auditorium on an authentic Wells Fargo stagecoach. He plays newspaper toss with shareholders, a game in which he is undefeated for ten years running. He allows his companies to display products and services on a trade show floor the size of three football fields. This is anything but another event. It's something to talk about. It has full-fledged bragging rights.

Bragging rights for your event might include a local celebrity hired to sign autographs and pose for pictures. It might include access to a restaurant or venue that is hard to reserve. Perhaps you bring people to a country club or yacht club that everyone wants to join. Simply hiring an emcee who is adored by the community, like the local news anchor or meteorologist, makes fine fodder for Facebook and Twitter posts. Ignore this principle at your event's peril.

Rule #4: Recognize Your Star Referrers

This is something most business owners are uncomfortable doing. They find my recommendation to recognize their star referrers as "tacky" or "cheesy." They ask me why they must give awards to grown adults. Obviously these people don't watch the Oscars, Grammys, or MVP awards after a major sporting event. Everyone wants to be recognized, whether they admit it or not. The ones who say they don't want the recognition will lie to you about other things. Likely, they are the ones who want recognition the most.

After saying a few opening remarks at your event and reminding everyone why you organized it in the first place, you must instruct them to return at a specific time for raffle prize announcements and a few special awards. Then recognize your top referrers with visible signs of your appreciation. Medals, trophies, plaques, and small but thoughtful gifts are not too much and certainly not as cheesy or tacky as you might imagine in your head. In fact, the number one source of emotional and personal thank-you notes come from those individuals who were recognized for their generosity toward your business. If people aren't reminding you after your event that they've never seen a business like yours before, then you're missing out on a critical opportunity to connect with your top referrers on a deeper level. Thank them and recognize them in front of your fans.

Rule #5: Set Clear Goals with the Right People On Board to Help You

Two ways to hold an *unsuccessful* referral event are to enter into the task without clear goals and to assume you can do it all by yourself. I mentioned earlier that I don't do events for my health. I have a private physician and a large, comfortable sailboat that help manage my health and blood pressure quite nicely, thank you. I do events to get more referrals. Period. We don't schedule an event or set a budget for that event until we have decided on clear and exciting goals. And you shouldn't either.

Sit down with your proposed event team and ask them how many new customers you think you could generate from an organized event. As a general rule of thumb, we can get about 10 to15 percent of an audience to drag a friend to an event and actually schedule a consultation for services with one of our brick-and-mortar pediatric dental or orthodontic clinics while they are at the event. If we want to get 50 new patient referrals, we anticipate an event for 500 people and set our budget based on what it takes to generate 50 new clients in our business. If you don't sit down and clearly articulate your goals with your team, you cannot expect them to execute the event successfully. In the final section of this chapter, I will walk you step-by-step through the process I use to help my team implement a successful event strategy.

DEMONSTRATE YOUR WORK FOR MASSIVE REFERRALS

One of the world's most prolific and profound classical musicians, Mozart worked constantly and at a lightning pace. He might write an entire symphony for a gig that was coming up the following week—so literally that fast. He wrote over 600 pieces, and he did it in under half of a lifetime. At the age of five, he wrote his first composition. By six, he was on the first of several European tours. A child prodigy, he interacted with the prominent musicians of his day and started studying their works. Many times, after hearing a piece played once, he would go home and transcribe the notes verbatim with only one or two edits. When Mozart was only thirteen years old, his father took him on an extended tour in Italy that lasted more than two years.

This was the life of a composer in mid-to-late 1700s. Go on tour, write feverishly, show your work to as many audiences as you can and raise funds for commissioned pieces. Mozart and his father didn't sit around waiting for people to discover them. Instead, they took their show on the road. And the results were outstanding. New aristocratic Europeans surfaced every week, providing new opportunities for Mozart to produce more work, and generating considerable wealth for his family.

How many business owners today would tirelessly commit to a two-year road show in a foreign country simply to provide opportunities to earn new business? What money is being left on the table for those businesses who fail to realize the power of event-based marketing? A significant sum and possibly much more.

Mozart and his father knew if they sat alone in their study, writing the next great piece of music and waiting for it to be discovered, the world might never know the genius of Mozart's work. Who is waiting to discover the great things about your business, and what are the odds they come knocking on your door demanding it from you? Find your opportunity today to invite more customers, patients, or donors to experience your work in a setting that encourages new business and repeat referrals. It's not going to happen while you are working alone in your study. You have to get out there and demonstrate what makes you different and why people should choose your business.

USE OTHER PEOPLE'S EVENTS TO GET MORE REFERRALS: THE ARTIST WHO BECAME EVERY COMPANY'S #1 EVENT ATTRACTION

Eileen McCoy is a successful portrait, landscape, and caricature artist who started working with corporate clients in a creative way. An award-winning artist and creative production artist at Hallmark Cards, Eileen found an interesting niche in hosting small and large events where she was the featured entertainment. Customers, patients, and donors at events all over Kansas City patiently wait in line for Eileen to create a caricature portrait of their kids or family. When we invite Eileen to one of our events, the line quickly wraps around the entire perimeter of the event space. Not only is she talented, but she's smart. Each caricature is branded for the event with a small logo and her information in the lower right corner of the artwork created before your very eyes. These portraits get framed and stay on the walls for years. Not surprisingly, her list of corporate clients has grown to an impressive roster of top area businesses.

How many of these corporate clients would have ever wandered into Eileen's art studio looking for a fun attraction for their next event or gala? The answer is somewhere between zero and not too many. How has she quickly grown another business inside her existing business simply by showing up at events and giving prospective new clients an opportunity to see her in a different light? Creating these settings where new customers can interact with you and see your work in a setting outside of the normal nine-to-five is critical to your success at generating word-of-mouth referrals.

In the space below, list three events you can attend this year that would allow you to demonstrate your business to prospective new customers. Circle a deadline on the calendar to schedule yourself at one of the events, and start generating more referrals. Write that deadline in the space below and hold yourself accountable.

1. _____

2. _____

3. _____

My deadline for attending the first event:

_____

Step #1: Define the Game—Implementation Time and How Rubber Meets Road with Events

You or your employees cannot win a game they don't know they are playing. Start by defining exactly what you're doing with this event. How many referrals do you currently receive per month? How many referrals per active customer do you receive each year? What is the conversion rate of those referrals to new customers, and how many of those new customers convert to new referrers? You are tracking these statistics in your business each month, correct?

Step #2: Set Your Baseline and Agree on Goals

I mentioned previously that successful events must have clear goals. To complement that principle, you must have accurate historical data. It's not realistic to expect your team to generate one hundred new referrals at an event if you've never held an event before and you only receive twenty referrals per year. Instead of guessing, go get the data.

Former New York City Mayor Rudy Giuliani was fond of saying "In God we trust. All others bring data." Establish your baseline for all the criteria you outlined in Step #1 when you Defined the Game. If you averaged fifteen new customer referrals per month last year, what would it look like if you increased that number to twenty or twenty-five? Think about how that might change your business.

After you've determined your baseline average for each metric from Step #1, you must sit down with your team and talk about what it will take to get the results you want. It might require the incentive of a team trip or outing. Perhaps a few extra days of paid vacation or a simple cash bonus will get your team excited to produce the results you want from the event. You won't know until you ask them, so schedule some time to sit down with your team and lay out the possible rewards for their results. Write them down, post them in the employee break areas, and add some fun reminders of the team goals leading up to the event.

Step #3: Decide Who Will Measure and When the Game Ends

Peter Drucker famously said, "If you can't measure it, you can't manage it." Somehow we always convince ourselves that things will just work out with all new initiatives. Things might work out, but things might also surprise you. The only way to know is to measure your results. Assign the responsibility of measurement to one of your employees or accept that responsibility yourself. Either way, don't design or run your event with blinders on. The amount of post-event follow up and offers made to capture more referrals often depends on the results during and immediately after the event.

If you don't have a product to sell at the event, you should be scheduling new customers for private consultations while at the event so they can come to a sales presentation or diagnostic call within the first few weeks afterwards. With accurate data, you can alert your team during the event and move forward after the event with the appropriate strategy to maximize your results.

For most events, we give our team a few weeks to wrap up loose ends, schedule new patients, and send follow-up communication to those who attended and those who referred. You decide when the game ends and be sure to announce the rewards from Step #2. Don't let the deadline slip quietly into the night. If you have to push hard leading up to it, push hard. Call, write, and email the customers who expressed an interest in your business. How many referrals did you anticipate getting, and how are you progressing toward your goals as you approach your deadline? Everyone in the company should be able to report those two numbers back to you on a daily basis.

Step #4: Celebrate the Wins and Repeat

My friend, marketing advisor and copywriter, Dan Kennedy, owns and races an impressive stable of horses throughout the year. He explained to me once, after we were discussing an employee management issue, that his stable hands will often give the same post-race feed mix and level of attention to the horses who lose as they do to those who win. What these employees are doing is confusing the hell out of the horses. Imagine what the horse is thinking, "If I win I get oats, and if I lose I get oats?" Even my dog knows when she chews up one of my socks that she's not getting a treat immediately afterwards.

> *Shower your team with praise and repeat the process. Leverage your wins.*

On the other hand, I see far too many business owners failing to reward results at all. As soon as a referral event is successful, they move right onto the next business event or project. Take some time to celebrate the wins. Sit down with your team; give praise and recognition publicly in front of other employees. Talk about the fun bonuses, trips, events, or time off that everyone just received and make a few notes on what could be improved next time. Shower your team with praise and repeat the process with errors eliminated. Leverage your wins.

NOW IS THE TIME

You've seen what event marketing can do for your business—or any business for that matter. Now is the time to take action. Review the principles, rules, and steps required to launch your first referral event, then go circle a date on the calendar. If you wait for the perfect time, it will never come. If you wait for the perfect event idea, you will never think of it. Done is always better than perfect, and there are new customers out there—as John Carlton says— "waiting for you in the ether."

Yes, you *can* receive more referrals in your business through event marketing. Now is the time.

CHAPTER SEVENTEEN
EMPLOYEE DELEGATION AND REFERRAL SYSTEM RESPONSIBILITIES

BY THIS POINT, YOUR HEAD MAY BE SPINNING WITH ALL THAT HAVING A REFERRAL SYSTEM entails. Yes, there is a lot that goes into it; there is no doubt about that. If you took on all the tasks associated with having an effective referral system, there may be little time left for you to see your patients and provide treatment. The good news is that you don't have to be the sole person who handles your referral system. There are other options available to you, and efficient business owners will always explore their options.

Time management is critical in business. There is no way you could do every job within your practice. Yet every person in your office serves an important role and is essential to the functioning of your business and in providing the best patient service. You filled those other roles with people who are highly qualified—or at least that's what you should have done—so you may want to fill this role with someone as well. The key to having your referral program be successful may lie in properly delegating this important task to someone who is a great match for the duties they will take on. It's such an important job that the duties shouldn't just be haphazardly handed to anyone.

WHAT TO LOOK FOR

You will want to look for some specific characteristics in the person you select to take on the role of managing your referral system. Look for someone who is quick on their feet, can talk in front of a group, and preferably has a strong green line on their Kolbe assessment. (If you are not already using the Kolbe, see Kolbe.com for details). Anecdotally, I've found employees from the service industry to be great at this type of position because they are used to working directly with customers and providing great service. They usually understand how to work with others and have a personality that does well in that environment.

When many of the large companies (such as Google and Facebook) hire today, they are not necessarily seeking a stellar resume filled with the best education and experiences. Sure, those things are nice, but there are other things that matter more. They want people who have a great personality, understand the company mission, and will have a little fun. Hiring a people person, which is what you will be doing for this role, means looking more for personality than experience. You can train people on the tasks their job will include, but a good attitude and the ability to get along well with others is not usually something that can be learned with training. Some people naturally have a gift for being good with other people. When you meet them, you feel their positive energy and that they are genuinely listening and interested. They are easy to get along with and have a sense of excitement. Someone like this is the kind of person who can help with your quest to build relationships for your practice.

It is generally believed that most people conducting job interviews make up their mind about a candidate within the first thirty seconds or so. Yet the interview may last fifteen minutes, thirty minutes, or even longer. So how does a person conducting the interview make up their mind within the first minute of meeting the candidate? Although a few people are influenced primarily by appearance, most people base this decision on attitude.

Your referral system is going to become the lifeline for your business growth. Choosing who should take on the task shouldn't be a decision you make lightly.

When you interact with someone, it takes only seconds to pick up on their energy and attitude. So when someone walks into an interview, that energy and attitude is quickly recognized and your brains kicks into a "yes" or "no" kind of mode. You may not even be aware that it's happening; it's just that fast.

The same goes for whomever you select to manage your referral system. When that person meets with area dentists, business owners, and others, those people will have an immediate yes or no kind of reaction, and they will either welcome them to provide more information, or find a way to push them aside. When you interview people for this position, pay close attention to your reaction within the first thirty seconds to a minute. The type of reaction you have is likely to be the same one that others will have if this person works on your behalf.

Ask yourself these questions and answer honestly. Will that person project a favorable image on your behalf? Does their personality invite people to want to hear more, or does it turn people off and send them in the other direction? As much as we like to believe that we don't judge people based on first impressions and the initial feelings we have when we meet them, that's exactly what happens. It happens in all of us, and it will happen with those they will work with on your behalf.

Your referral system is going to become the lifeline for your business growth. Choosing who should take on the task shouldn't be a decision you make lightly. Put some time into ensuring you make a solid choice. That's your first step in having a successful referral system that helps you reach your goals.

You may find that the person who is perfect for these duties already works for you. If so, great! That saves time in recruiting and bringing the person up to speed. If they don't already work for you, then put in the time to find the right person to join your team. Have patience so you do it right, rather than being in a hurry to get the position filled. Otherwise you'll be compromising on the quality of hire. Act as if your business growth and future depends on it, because in a lot of ways it truly does.

POSITION FILLED

Once you have decided who your referral system duties will be delegated to, it's time to get down to business. If the person is a new hire, they first need to learn the ins and outs of your practice. They should know the history, your mission, business principles, etc. They can only sell your name if they know what you do, why you do it, and everything about your practice. Let this person get to know you and your team, as well as the office. They need to feel confident about their knowledge of your office in order to share it with others, so provide them with the information and help them understand your niche.

Armed with information and understanding, your new referral facilitator can jump right into the mix of things. Have this employee make a list of every doctor, business, dental hygienist, and family that currently refers to your practice, and set up a system to be in front of those people physically at least twice per year. The previous chapter on events gives you a great way to get in front of large groups of people in one setting. Be sure to single out your VIP referrals and give them special access to your events, preregistration, special seating, special recognition, etc.

The employee who takes on the referral role position can help you identify, track, and schedule time spent with each of your VIPs. This is often an area that is difficult for doctors to keep up with, so letting someone else manage the details will allow you to still get everything done and meet all of your plans and goals for the referral system.

Another first task is to take a list of at least ten new dentists, physicians, businesses, and families that aren't currently referring to you, but you'd like to see them start. Then incentivize the employee to go make that happen. Remember, not all employees want more money in their jobs—although many do. They may want more autonomy in how they get their results, the ability to master something new, and a higher purpose than just punching a time clock or putting in another day at the office. Find ways to make their role as referral ambassador a job they are proud to accomplish, even if they only work on your referral system part-time.

Speaking of part-time, you don't have to feel as though you need to hire someone or delegate these duties to someone full-time. This, especially in the beginning, can be a part-time gig. If you put the right person in the position, you may never need it to become anything more than part-time. You will make that determination as you go along and watch it in action. If you want to increase the hours and duties, great; if not, you can stay at a comfortable place that still provides you with the ability to meet your referral goals each month and year.

DELEGATION FEAR

Before we get deeper into the idea of delegating your referral system tasks, let's take a moment to look at the fear of delegation. Most entrepreneurs realize that delegating can be a good thing, but many also shy away from doing so. In fact, the *Harvard Business Review* reports that delegation remains one of the most underutilized and underdeveloped management capabilities. They referenced a 2007 study on the topic which found that out of 332 companies surveyed, half of them had concerns about their employees' delegation skills. Even so, only 28 percent of them offered any type of training to their employees to improve their delegation skills.

Considering this information, it's no wonder so many people hold back when it comes to delegation. People fear it largely because they don't necessarily know how to go about delegating duties. They also have trust issues, causing them to fear that the delegated tasks won't get done properly or as well as they would like them to be. Consequently, many people hoard work. You may do this or see others in your offices who do it. Delegating work may seem difficult at first; but once you get the hang of it and overcome those fears, you will appreciate all that delegation can do for your practice. You may even find that you like it so much you want to delegate more often.

If you are not delegating, perhaps it is time to be honest and ask yourself why. Get real by coming up with the true reason you're holding back. Also, consider the real cost of what holding back could be doing to your practice. In order to grow, you need people around you who help in many capacities. There is no way you can do everything on your own.

Delegating and giving people some space to do what you have asked them to do may turn out surprisingly well for your office. Most employees want to please you and do a great job. Let them develop their critical thinking skills so they can find ways to help you meet the goals you have set for them.

As time passes, you will be able to evaluate whether or not you have the right person in this position. Take stock of whether goals are being met, how well the person is motivated for the tasks at hand, and if your referrals are increasing. Changes can be made as you go along.

Also, if you are going to delegate referral tasks, be sure that you are not piling too much on one person. If they have time to take it on along with their other job duties, then great. If not, they will feel overwhelmed, which will obviously work against you. Keep tabs on whether or not they have too much piled on them. Perhaps they can shift part of their duties to someone else in the office. No matter how you work it out, it's important that your employees are not overwhelmed, or you will not get the productivity and effectiveness out of them that you are seeking. While you are ensuring they are not overwhelmed, avoid micromanaging them and the tasks you have delegated to them. Nobody likes to be micromanaged. While some managers may feel micromanaging helps get things done, it really increases stress levels and likely reduces productivity.

> *If you are not delegating, perhaps it is time to be honest and ask yourself why. Get real by coming up with the true reason you're holding back.*

Look for someone who is ready from the start to take on the responsibilities. If you hire the right person, you can trust they will do the tasks to your liking and will be effective in their position.

EFFECTIVE VERSUS POOR DELEGATION

It's easy to simply delegate your referral responsibilities, but the act of delegating *effectively* may be totally different. When you delegate referral responsibilities—or hire someone for the position—you will find that they are either going to be effective in their position or end up being a poor fit. You want the first one, obviously; and it's important to get the right person handlingthis areaof the practice.

After picking the best person to delegate your referral system tasks to, it's time to trust them. The work needs to be done correctly and well, but give them some space to try and do it their way. They may have ideas for how they would like to go about working toward the goals you have set before them. Give them the opportunity to try out their own ideas and see if they work. Trusting in your referral ambassador and their ability will be of greater benefit to you than immediately vetoing their ideas.

The person who takes this on can only do their job well if they know clearly what you expect from them. Determine what their tasks and goals will be so you can provide them with that insight. Give them enough guidance so they know which way to head, but not so much that you are hand-holding them to get there.

The best way to determine if the person is doing their job effectively is to set some benchmarks and evaluate them at various time frames. Setting milestones will keep you both on track and aware if things are headed in the right direction. These benchmarks can be the number of new referrals per week or month, how many new dentists begin referring to your office, or any other goals you set. The specific benchmarks themselves are not as important as the fact that you set some, follow up on them, and use the information gathered from the evaluation to see if your referral system is effective or not.

When you see that this person is effectively carrying out the tasks, recognize them publicly. Giving them kudos in front of your team or in your monthly newsletter will help keep them motivated and feeling good about what they are doing.

It's also a good idea to let your team know that this person will be taking on a role that handles referral duties. Keeping everyone up to speed on this will help with the cohesiveness of the office, and they may have their own ideas of how to assist the person in their duties.

In their book, *Out of the Question: How Curious Leaders Win,* Guy Parsons and Allan Milham explain some of the traits great leaders have. Among them is that they don't dictate. On the contrary, effective leaders know how to bring out the best in people and give them the space they need to do the work. A good leader, they say, will share the objectives and goals with the employee, but be open to how the employee feels they should go about reaching those goals.

This is a far cry from how many people lead: by giving step-by-step instructions on every little thing. Great leaders don't hand-hold; they communicate what outcomes they would like, but then they allow the employee some creative leeway in reaching those objectives. Everyone works in different ways and people have their strengths and weaknesses. It's an asset to have someone who knows how to go about getting things done, despite their weaknesses.

Additionally, the authors point out that great leaders are open to input from anyone. People don't need to be in a high position in order to have their ideas considered. When you can take ideas from anyone on your team and consider them all equally, you are bound to come across some good ones you may not have been exposed to otherwise. An equal playing field in this regard eliminates the issues of titles and ranks and opens the door to ideas that can effectively help your practice grow.

It's also a good idea to create an environment where everyone knows all ideas are welcome and considered. That way everyone feels safe sharing them. A safe environment helps get creativity flowing, and that's always a good force for helping to move your practice forward.

STRATEGIC DELEGATION

Wright State University offers information about how to delegate strategically. They suggest that although very few managers excel at delegation, effective delegation will reduce the managers' workload and provide growth opportunities. With delegation being such an important asset to your practice, it's a good idea to learn how to become good at it. They suggest that when you delegate strategically, you are using forethought and planning in a way that will capitalize on opportunities.

In order to delegate strategically and help your employee be effective with their referral system duties, you will want to devise a plan. Start by determining what the objectives will be, let them know how much flexibility they have in using their own discretion in achieving them, and get them involved in helping to create the plan for how goals will be accomplished and how progress will be evaluated.

While we are on the topic, let's look at a few things people can do to bring out the best in others. Telling someone to be a good leader is a lot different than giving them some specific ideas of things they can do to be one.

Good leaders tend to focus on the person's strengths. Think of a baseball coach. The coach is unlikely to put someone in a key position who is not fit for it. If he knows the player's strength lies in hitting home runs, the coach isn't going to put the player in the cleanup spot of the batting order; if the player is a fast runner, he won't put him in the outfield. A good coach considers both strengths and weaknesses to help his players perform at their best so they can bring the most benefit to the team and help the entire team become more successful

Delegating takes time and effort, but if you create a plan and carry it out, you will likely have great success. Your referral program will benefit from having someone caring for it who understands the mission, can think creatively about how to make connections and build relationships, and is excited to help you grow your practice.

POOR DELEGATION

Now that you have an idea of what effective delegation looks like, let's consider what poor delegation may look like. The more you know about poor delegation, the more you can steer clear of it and keep things on the right path.

Poor delegation usually starts with not really wanting to delegate in the first place—or not having a clear idea of what it means to delegate effectively and strategically. I delegate a lot in my practice and all that I do. I have to, or I would have a difficult time getting everything done effectively and growing my practice. Like most people, I didn't go into the practice of delegating knowing how to do it effectively or strategically. It was something I learned about, and the learning continued throughout the process.

I have learned some things through trial and error, and other things I've learned from reading on the topic, listening to others, and a variety of other ways. If you pay attention, the person you are delegating things to can help you learn a lot about delegation. They will be demonstrating what works, what doesn't, what makes people more effective and productive, and so much more.

Poor delegation happens when you don't have a plan or understanding, when you don't give the person a clear picture of what you need done. They can't possibly get the tasks done if they don't have a good idea of what the task is.

This reminds me of the Seinfeld episode where George's boss delegates a project to him, but George has no idea what the project is or how to go about completing it. In that episode, called "The Bottle Deposit," George's boss explains the details of a project he wants George to work on, but as he is explaining it, he walks into the restroom. Assuming George followed him in, he continues to explain the details and instructions for carrying out the project. The problem is that George never followed his boss into the restroom, assuming he would continue the directions when he was finished. But when his boss exits the restroom, he is finished providing the project directives, which of course leaves George clueless.

Although George realizes his boss apparently continued to provide the details for the project while in the restroom, he can't bring himself to tell him he missed it all. He doesn't want his boss to think he wasn't paying attention. This sets him on a course of having no idea how to carry out the project. He has no clue what the objectives are or where to start, which means he has to discover the details about the project without letting his boss know he doesn't actually know what's going on. Although it's a comedy and we can laugh about it happening with George, it's not so funny when this happens in the real business world.

When you delegate a project or task to someone, you are setting them up for failure if you don't make sure that they know all of the details. They need to know the information so they feel confident in getting started, carrying out the tasks, and striving to meet your goals. Avoid setting your employee up for failure. Do your part to make sure they understand the task at hand.

Poor delegation usually starts with not really wanting to delegate in the first place—or not having a clear idea of what it means to delegate effectively and strategically.

If you are going to make the decision to delegate your referral management, take the steps to do it right. If you don't, you will never get what you want and need out of a referral system. The only way your referral system can be effective and successful is if whoever is managing it completely understands the mission and how to go about pulling it off. Whether they use their own creative ways to do it, or they take your advice and follow it exactly, they need to know where you want to go in order to help you get there.

In the consulting I do, working one-on-one with orthodontists around the nation, I have helped many learn how to delegate properly. While some are skeptical at first, once they get started, they usually end up seeing the beauty of effective and strategic delegation. My guess is that you will, too.

MY OWN EMPLOYEE DELEGATION

Since I am comfortable with delegating strategically and effectively, I also had someone take on much of my referral system responsibilities. Mark was someone who was going back to nursing school and working part-time in a dental office on Saturdays. We found him through a friend, and he was always the life of the party. He had the type of stand-out and get-along personality that I mentioned earlier. People wanted to know Mark because of his great personality.

He was so good with people that we hired him part-time to do our referral system deliveries and build rapport with our referring offices and businesses. Mark hit the ground running with a clear understanding of what we were after and ideas for how to go about making it happen.

I followed my own advice in tracking and evaluating how effective his efforts were. What I found is that the return on investment was well beyond 10:1. This showed me that it wasn't that I couldn't afford to hire someone to take on these dedicated responsibilities, I couldn't afford *not* to. Without Mark working his magic, I was leaving money on the table. A lot of money. Having him engage in the referral responsibilities helped build long-lasting relationships with a variety of referral sources.

Now that you have learned what is involved in having a successful referral system, you may be realizing that hiring or delegating the responsibilities to someone is your best course of action. After all, you can continue doing what you do well, while you make a small monetary investment toward bringing in more referrals. It has paid off well for me, and if done correctly, it should also pay off for you as well.

NEVER STOP PROSPECTING

At times you or your referral manager may feel as though you have tapped everyone you can tap in your area. It may feel like that, but I am a firm believer in the idea that there are always more areas to prospect. As I have shown in prior chapters, you can go well beyond local dentists in order to reach other potential referral sources; there are plenty of other medical professionals and businesses to consider.

You and your referral manager want to develop a referral mindset. That way, you are always considering which direction to tap next for potential referral sources. They are truly all around you and often available for the taking. It's just a matter of noticing them, taking action, and seeing it through.

Keep in mind that prospecting is always going to be a numbers game. The more places and people you contact regarding referrals, the higher percentage of new sources and total referrals you are going to get. By tracking the details of how many people are counted and how many referrals come in, you can even come up with the ratio it takes you so you get an idea of how many people your referral manager needs to contact in order to get a particular number of referrals.

Delegating these responsibilities to the *right* person is crucial, because they are either going to greatly benefit your business or hold you back. They'll either bring in more referrals or leave money on the table. How this is all handled is in your hands. The process can be changed and revised as you go along, providing the person doesn't do irreparable harm to a potential referral source relationship. But still, don't let the fear of what could happen hold you back. Every month you go without having someone taking on referral duties is another month of missed referrals. The sooner you act, and act appropriately and strategically, the better.

Here are a few delegation tips to help you be more effective:

- **Have a clear idea of what you want the person to do and to achieve.** It's difficult for people to reach goals if nobody knows what they are. Write down what the person will do and what the ultimate goals are.
- **Find the *right* person to take on the task.** If you don't match the task to the person correctly, then you probably won't end up with the results you are seeking. Finding the right person for the project is essential to its overall success. While considering the person's skills so they can complete the tasks at hand, also consider their personality. In a referral management position, you want someone who is a people person.
- **Identify what tasks need to be done, but don't feel you need to tell the person exactly how to do them.** Some tasks may require you to explain things to them, but they will also likely have their own input on how to go about achieving something. Be open to listening to their ideas for achieving the goals.
- **Make sure you explain what the goals are to the person you are delegating to.** They need to have a thorough understanding of what's expected in order to pull it off. Left without direction, they will accomplish very little.

- **Set up a way to monitor the plan so you can both see if the project is moving in the right direction.** You should have milestones that can be evaluated to determine if things are progressing properly. From there you can make changes as you go along.
- **Back off and give the person some space so they can get to work on the project.** Let them know you are there if they have questions but that you trust they can handle things. While it's okay to check in to see how things are going, it's not okay to smother the person or try to micromanage everything they are doing.
- **Give praise where it is due.** If your referral manager brings in referrals, let your office know about it. That will be a great boost of confidence for the person to keep doing more of what they're doing.

CHAPTER EIGHTEEN

EMPLOYEE INCENTIVES WITH A FOCUS ON MASTERY, AUTONOMY, AND PURPOSE

IN THE BUSINESS WORLD, MOST PEOPLE SEEM TO THINK THAT IF YOU THROW MORE MONEY at a something, conditions will improve. People try to pay their employees more, offer them attractive bonuses, and even dangle stock in front of them. All this in an effort to get more productivity out of them. It may or may not work, though, because there's no hard and fast rule that says money is the answer to motivating people to do more. In fact, for many people, money doesn't seem to help at all to motivate them or increase their productivity.

UNDERSTANDING TODAY'S EMPLOYEES

When we look at the research from Barry Schwartz at Swarthmore College on doing the right thing for the right reason, we learn that a large body of evidence has been established which explains that in today's complex business environment, simply throwing more money at people is not an effective way to motivate performance.

What we are learning about the next generation of employees is that they value experience over things by a large margin. So waving some money at them may not be the key to getting them excited about doing their job. They care more about the experience of doing their job. They want to enjoy it and personally get something out of the activities involved. Adding a few bucks per hour to their salary isn't going to help them enjoy their position more. They are after the experience, not necessarily the big bucks.

The research from Schwartz and his colleagues, reported in his book *Practical Wisdom,* demonstrates that employees are at their highest engagement within the company when they are mastering something new, have autonomy in how they get their results, and are attached to a higher purpose. This seems like there's a lot that goes into this formula, but if you nail it just right, you will have employees who are highly productive and help further your practice's success and growth. It's a goal well worth setting and going after because it ultimately benefits everyone in your office.

Let's take a more in-depth look at each of these three areas to get an idea of what they would look like in action in your office.

MASTERY

It is human nature to want to be good at something. Anything, really. We just have to be good at something or we begin to feel less valuable. When we improve our skills and become masters at something, we become more confident; and that positively affects all areas of our life. It doesn't matter if it's learning to master something in the workplace or a hobby, just by getting better and becoming a master at doing something, we experience far-reaching benefits.

We all want to be good at something. That's why mastery should be an area you focus on with your employees. Stay with me here for a moment, because even though it seems like this has nothing to do with the employee's job, it really does. There are companies out there that encourage their employees to go learn things outside of their job. Things, actually, that have nothing to do with their job. That's because they get it; they understand that by mastering something, the employee will become more productive in the workplace, too.

> *When we improve our skills and become masters at something, we become more confident; and that positively affects all areas of our life.*

Take, for example, the popular outdoor company REI and what they did on Black Friday in 2015. It's the most popular shopping day of the year. Stores around the nation are geared up and ready to take care of shoppers who are eager to spend their money on gifts for people for the upcoming holiday season. Rather than schedule more people to work that day, the company announced ahead of time that they would be closing their doors on Black Friday.

A hush fell over the country when that announcement hit because it seemed so bizarre to most people. How could a popular store possibly close their doors on the busiest shopping day of the year? And why would they even consider doing it in the first place? Didn't they realize they will be missing out on sales and their customers will most likely just do their shopping elsewhere that day?

Well, it may have been a scary and bold move for the company, but it's one they stuck with. When they decided to close their doors, it was because they said they wanted all of their employees to spend the day outdoors. In fact, their CEO stated "We believe that being outside makes our lives better." He wanted all of his employees to take the day off and go spend it outdoors, enjoying life, rather than being caught up in the hustle and bustle of Black Friday shopping and all the stress that comes with it.

Again, going for experience over money. He didn't give them all a raise on Black Friday or say that the store would share in the profits from any extra sales numbers generated on that day. What hc did is give his employees an experience and encouraged them to get outdoors, to go master their love of outdoor activities, whether it be running, biking, hiking, or kayaking. REI paid their 12,000 employees to take the busiest shopping day of the year off and use that time to take care of themselves by spending some time outdoors.

Did it hurt their company? Not a chance. It actually did quite the opposite. Their employees loved the idea of getting paid to go spend the day hiking, and their customers respected the fact that they opted out of the frenzy which takes place every Black Friday. Not only did their employees enjoy the day, but many likely worked on some of their outdoor skills as well, and they came back to work feeling great. That experience very likely helped them be better employees upon their return. Their customers didn't run to another outdoor company; instead they probably did some online shopping at the REI store, and then waited until another day to stop in their store.

I'm not suggesting you close your doors on the busiest day of the year or during the busiest time. What I am saying is that by having your employees do something else, you will end up getting better employees. Their productivity and engagement will improve as a result of them doing something else and mastering something different, whether it's going hiking or becoming a great clog dancer. The closer they get to mastering something, the better the employee you will get.

There are many big companies that do neat things to help their employees become better at their jobs by encouraging things that don't actually pertain to their jobs. Google is another company known for the perks they provide their employees. Not only are employees encouraged to be active, such as leaving the desk and taking a run or riding a scooter around the campus. They also give their employees paid time off to go explore other passions they may have. Imagine getting paid time off, outside of your vacation time, so you can explore your passion for mountain climbing? No matter what it is, you get some time to master it; and they are happy to have you do it, even on their time.

At Burleson Orthodontics & Pediatric Dentistry, we pay employees up to four hours per week (10 percent of their work week) to go learn something new. They could use that time to go take a pottery class, attend an improv comedy training course, or simply sit in bed under the covers reading on a rainy Saturday morning. As long as they are learning something new that is not related to orthodontics or pediatric dentistry, we pay them for it when they report back to the entire group at the next monthly meeting and provide a quick synopsis of what they are learning.

Doing things like this helps your employees with mastery. It helps them improve their quality of life, and they learn new skills and ways of thinking. Sometimes people have the best ideas when they are out on the golf course or taking a run. Things like this improve creativity and self-confidence and open new doors. Your employees will feel great, which in turn is going to help your office do great.

One way to help your employees become great at their jobs is to get them to go do something else. You will be surprised at how engaged they are when they return. Their productivity will improve, which definitely makes this effort well worth it.

When you encourage your employees to do this and even help make it easier for them to do by giving them the time to do it, you are fostering lifelong learning. What we know about lifelong learners is that they are people who are always in pursuit of knowledge. They tend to have better skills when it comes to getting along with others, and they are more resilient, intelligent, and appreciative. Your practice will always benefit from having employees who are lifelong learners, even if what they are learning doesn't directly relate to their field. They are learning a variety of skills that will benefit them in all areas of their life, including when they are on the job.

> One way to help your employees become great at their jobs is to get them to go do something else—their productivity will improve.

It is estimated that around 69 percent of employees are disengaged at their jobs today. That's a lot of people who are not completely tuned in to what they are doing. The more we can get those employees engaged, the better off we will all be. Encouraging mastery of something in each of your employees is a great way to get them more engaged when they are on the job.

AUTONOMY

Take a moment and think about some of the jobs you had prior to entering your current professional field. Did you ever have a job where your duties were so spelled out for you that there was no room for you to ever use your own creativity or decision-making skills to figure anything out? How about having a manager who micromanaged you to the point where you felt like they were still over your shoulder when you went to the restroom? Scenarios like these happen all too often, and they are dreadful.

Employees do not do well when they are under the microscope or when their hand is held every step of the way when performing their job. Yes, they need proper training so they know what their job is or how to use things like your contact management system. Beyond that, though, they don't need or want to be treated like they are a child who can't find their way back from the lunchroom. While this may seem overly simplistic, you would be surprised at some of the hand-holding and micromanaging I've seen people do over the years. I can tell you without a doubt that it's counterproductive and does not help you reach goals. In fact, it often works in just the opposite way; it holds your employee and office back.

> *When you give your employees autonomy, you are empowering them. Autonomy gives them the power to work the way they want to work.*

When you give your employees autonomy, you are empowering them, which is something they will truly appreciate. Autonomy gives them the power to work the way they want to work. They will have a voice in being able to determine the best way for them to meet the goals you have set for them. By being able to use their creativity, skills, and self-direction to determine the best course of action, they will become more productive. Your employees will also be happier, more satisfied with their work experience, and more likely to help elevate the game of other employees around them.

There are a lot of benefits to giving your employees autonomy, yet many company owners and managers fear doing this. They feel that if they don't micromanage everything that gets done, if they don't give exact directions on how to do it, then things will fall short of being what they wanted. Those leaders are holding themselves and their companies back in a big way.

Think about it this way for a moment. You hired the people in your office because you thought they were competent people who could perform the job which they were hired to do. If that is the case, then why would you ever need to hand-hold or micromanage? If you think you have employees who need you by their side every second, telling them what to do and how to do it, then it just may be time to start finding some new employees. You have to start with hiring the right people to begin with. And once you have them in the position, give them some space to do their thing.

In order for you to provide your employees with autonomy, you need to hire the right people, be clear about what their job goals are, and then turn them loose. Let them decide the best way for them to accomplish the goals you have set. Software companies are one industry that have figured this out. They let their software engineers know what it is they want, what the end product will be; but then they give their employees some space. That way the people can go about writing the software in the manner that makes sense to them. Maybe they work best when they are at home in their pajamas at two in the morning. If that's the case, it is a good idea to let them do it that way. You wouldn't get the same productivity out of them at two in the afternoon in the office in a suit and tie.

> *Autonomy gives people the ability to call the shots while meeting your ultimate goals at the same time.*

Autonomy gives people the ability to call the shots while meeting your ultimate goals at the same time. Give them the address where they need to be and a time frame to show up but don't tell them which roads to take, what their speed should be, and whether or not they can drink a bottle of water as they are driving.

Give your employees autonomy so they can do what they want in the way they want to do it to get the job done, but also let them know you are there for support if they need you. While most employees will appreciate autonomy, you may come across one who finds that freedom makes them a bit anxious. This is because they don't yet trust their own abilities to be able to work in an autonomous environment. Perhaps this is one of their first jobs or they have worked in previous jobs where they were micromanaged, and they have gotten used to that type of work environment. Give them some time, and they will adjust and most likely come to love having more creativity and say in how their day goes.

If your referral system director wants to do some work from home because that helps him stay focused and energized, let him do it. If he have suggestions on how to improve something, be sure to listen. In our company, flex time for projects is a great example. I don't care if you are at home, at the office, or sitting on a beach when making outbound phone calls to get doctors registered for an open house. If the activity improves the results, we encourage and leverage the activity.

Employees who have autonomy are almost always going to outperform those who do not. They will have more confidence and feel they are more a part of what they are doing. They are more likely to give more, which in turn produces more.

Researchers have found that across cultures, having autonomy in the workplace is important to employees. It has positive benefits for both the employee and the company. Those who have more autonomy at work will tend to be more loyal to their employer, perform better, be more engaged, and be more productive. It's also been shown that businesses that give their employees autonomy will have a lower turnover rate, which also saves you money in the long run.

If you have been the type of manager who hasn't been giving your employees autonomy, have no fear. It is never too late to make changes and become the type of leader who does. Begin by letting your employees know that you would like them to become more involved in calling the shots and in making some of the decisions about how to get things done. You can make the change all at once, or you can gradually let go of things and let the transition take place more slowly. Either way, you will notice a big difference in your team when you get to the point where they have autonomy. They will be happier, more satisfied at work, and likely much more productive. People who are satisfied and happy with where they work will go out of their way to go above and beyond for their employer. Be the kind of employer who makes employees want to be loyal and go above and beyond.

It is sometimes easier to see how appreciated autonomy will be if you can imagine yourself in their shoes. Like the old saying goes, treat others how you want to be treated. You would never want anyone micromanaging you eight hours per day, or standing over your shoulder telling you how to do every little task. Nobody else does either. When everyone has some space and can help choose their own direction, things go smoother for everyone involved.

PURPOSE

In a one-month period in 2014, Starbucks employees donated over 232,000 hours to service projects in their own communities. The company encourages their employees to get active volunteering in their own community. Their employees volunteer hours every year in every community they happen to be in. They volunteer to help with areas that have been devastated, assist with environmental work, and more. Encouraging their employees to volunteer in their community is something that works for them, as well as many other companies around the world.

Some companies offer their employees incentives to get out and volunteer in their community. At Deloitte, they give their employees an unlimited number of hours to volunteer. They encourage them to put those hours into education and veteran programs or other places that will help make a long-term impact. The technology company Salesforce gives their employees forty-eight hours of paid time off each year so they can use that time to volunteer. The company estimates that their employees have donated over a million volunteer hours. PCL Construction gives their employees fifty paid hours per year to go volunteer. The employees end up putting their building skills to use in their community, building homes for Habitat for Humanity, painting, and more. They also hold a volunteer recognition luncheon each year where employees are recognized for volunteering their time.

Companies such as Starbucks and Costco are really good at this. They want their employees to be out there helping in the community, and they understand that when people do good things, more good comes back to them. It is a way of giving back to the community that helped make their business a success. Giving back makes people feel good, and it helps the area that they live in—or wherever they may be doing the volunteering. This isn't just for religious or nonprofit institutions.

At Burleson Orthodontics and Pediatric Dentistry, we have been paying employees forty hours per year (one additional paid week of vacation) to take a mission trip or volunteer somewhere locally. Soup kitchens have been filled, summer Bible school classes have been taught, and Habitat for Humanity houses have been built from the efforts of employees at our practice. The employee gets to pick what they want to contribute their time to and we support their efforts. It is our community, and together we are all helping support it and make it great.

When you attach your people to a purpose bigger than themselves, you have a business that not only makes a difference in the world, but a business that does better. I can't place a tangible number on the way this works, but it just works. I don't question it. I just follow what works; and getting your people excited about making a difference in the world absolutely, positively works.

Research conducted in this area seems to find that the reason it may work is that when people volunteer, it helps grow their heart. They care more and want to help their community more; and when people engage in altruistic activities, they tend to feel good about themselves. According to researchers, volunteering has even been found to be one of the activities people can do to increase happiness in their lives as a whole. It gives people a sense of purpose and improves their overall quality of life.

Not only does volunteering benefit people in their personal lives, but it also translates to their professional life. Those who volunteer tend to be more engaged when they are at the workplace. They are more caring about their workplace environment and with getting along with their fellow team members, and they are more ambitious.

Volunteering is a good morale booster, too. If you don't believe it, get your team together one weekend to help

When you attach your people to a purpose bigger than themselves, you have a business that not only makes a difference in the world, but a business that does better.

build a home or collect coats for the homeless during the winter. Observe how it brings your team together and boosts their spirit. People feel as though they are participating in something larger than themselves, and it brings purpose to their life. It makes people feel good about giving back to their community and making a positive change.

The benefits of people volunteering their time are well documented. But the problem for many people is that they simply don't feel as though they have the time to volunteer because they work a full-time job. This is why many businesses today are giving employees paid time off so they can use those hours to volunteer. Granted, some people may feel as though they are not truly volunteering then, because to volunteer one's time it means they are doing so without receiving money in return. But the employees are not receiving money for volunteering; we are paying them so that they have the ability to make volunteering a part of their lives each year. For many people, if their schedule is too busy, the one thing that is going to be dropped first is volunteering. We don't want that, and neither do other companies, so we give our employees the time they need to make a positive change in the community.

Consider what type of purpose you can give your employees. Could you also give them a week off each year with those hours to be dedicated to volunteering in the community? Do you have a few specific types of charities you would like them to choose from? Determine what you would like to do and how you would offer it to your employees. It is best if you can give them a chance to choose from several types of charities so they still have some control over what they are doing in the community. Maybe they can help a homeless shelter, Habitat for Humanity, a local school, animal shelter, or hospital. In today's world, there is a huge need for volunteers. We love to encourage our employees to get out there and get active in the community. It's good for them and their soul and ends up being good for us, too. When they feel good about what they are doing, they tend to be happier employees who are more engaged and productive. They respect the fact that we give them that week to volunteer, which also helps create more loyalty and keep turnover rates lower.

Giving your employees a sense of purpose will go a long way toward helping your community, helping them personally, and helping your practice. When they feel good about what they are doing, it will translate to more goodness in your business, too.

This is also a program you should be proud of and share with your community. Let people know that your team gives back to the community by volunteering. Write it up and post about it on your website, take pictures of your employees and post about it on your social media sites, and get the word out. Keep track of what they do and where they decide to do it. Hold a special lunch or breakfast each year where you recognize the volunteer efforts your employees contributed to the community. This is a good thing and should not go unrecognized by you, your team, or the community as a whole. Keep track of how many volunteer hours your team puts in each year, and send out a yearly press release letting local media know that number.

Consider what type of purpose you can give your employees. We love to encourage our employees to get out there and get active in the community. It's good for them and their soul and ends up being good for us, too.

Many good things can result from creating a volunteer program at your practice. Along with helping to create a sense of purpose, your good deeds will not go unnoticed. The universe will reward you. People will notice everything your team is doing, and good things will come your way.

Remember that the world is like a magnet. What we send out is what comes back to us. If we put out good things, are helpful in our community, and do things to strengthen our community, those things come back to us.

And our community is helpful and strengthens us, too. That's just the way that it works. I may not know exactly how it happens, but I do know that it works, and I've seen it working for many years. There is a reason why so many companies today are giving their employees paid time off to go volunteer in their community. Every time they do it, their business benefits, too. You can't go wrong with that.

PUTTING IT ALL TOGETHER

If you want to give incentives to your employees, particularly the ones that will be taking care of your referral program, keep these things in mind. Mastery, autonomy, and purpose are three of the ingredients that are needed to have a successful outcome. In order for your practice to be successful in getting more referrals, you need someone who is engaged, who knows their community and cares about it, and who feels they have a sense of purpose. These are three things you can provide your employees by giving them time to engage in something they love, giving them the ability to call some of the shots when they do their job, and by encouraging them to put in some time volunteering in the community.

Your employees want to do a good job for you, they really do. Being a good leader is not about putting your thumb on them and holding them down until they achieve goals. A good leader empowers those who work on the team, giving them the ability to find ways to achieve goals all on their own. Sure, you are there on the sidelines in case there are questions or a little guidance is needed, but you will be pleasantly surprised at the wonderful results your office can achieve when you give your employees some room for mastery, autonomy, and purpose. They will end up being employees who will be loyal and want to help you achieve your goals, and they will feel valued at your practice. A satisfied employee is one who will go above and beyond to help grow your practice and make your patients love your office.

Mastery, autonomy, and purpose are three of the ingredients that are needed to have a successful outcome.

When it comes to your referral manager, these things are especially important. They are going to be working with people in the community on your office's behalf. The more they can feel good about themselves, contribute to their community, master something, and figure out how to reach those goals using their preferred methods, the more your office is going to benefit.

You need someone who is going to be engaged in what they are doing on your behalf. Having an employee who experiences mastery, autonomy, and purpose will do just that. They will become far more valuable employees for you when they experience those things.

Your referral managers will have a purpose in your office when they understand what their job is, what is expected of them, and how they are contributing to growing your practice. When they see the direct results that their efforts make, they will work harder to see even more results come about. Everyone loves to see that the work they do pays off and matters. An engaged referral manager is going to offer people a sense of confidence and caring in the community, and it will be on your behalf. Yes, you want to have great expectations for them. But no, you shouldn't give them a specific, detailed plan for how to accomplish everything. Give them some space to let them use their own creativity to make things happen.

Now that you will have your referral manager on autopilot, you also want to do one more thing. Schedule a meeting with that person on a regular basis. It doesn't have to be lengthy; but even ten minutes once per week will have an impact. Gather for those few minutes so they can keep you up to date on what they are working on, and you can both discuss ideas about how to keep blazing that referral trail that has people ringing your phone.

CHAPTER NINETEEN

LOCAL NONPROFIT OR CHARITY PROGRAMS AND ESTABLISHING YOUR COMPELLING REASON WHY

IF YOU KNEW THAT A COMPANY IN YOUR AREA WAS INVOLVED IN GIVING BACK BY SUPPORTING local charities, would you be more inclined to do business with them? If you are like most people, you probably would. What I have found over the years is that parents and patients who have money want to spend it with companies that make a difference. Does your company make a difference? If not, you may want to change that—the sooner the better.

When I speak with other orthodontists about being involved in local charity, they automatically assume they should pick a dozen charities in the area to start supporting. While that may be the approach people first think of, it's not the approach I want you to take. Being involved in so many different charities would going to water down the message and the effectiveness of what you are trying to do to help them.

WHAT TO SUPPORT

Your practice should find one charity you can really support in a big way. This is a more effective approach than diluting your efforts and giving small amounts to many charities. Choose to give a lot to one big charity. Or take it a step further and form your own charity, which is what we did with the Rheam Foundation for Cleft and Craniofacial Orthodontics.

Our charity provides orthodontic care to low income families in our area with children who were born with cleft palate or other craniofacial anomalies. Our mission is to change lives, advance the profession, and support our community. The charity's namesake is my grandfather, who set a great example of the importance of serving others and helping the community.

We have helped many charities over the years. We see all of the great work that is done and who benefits from our time and efforts. We also accept donations from the community to help support our mission. Our charity gives us one more way we are involved in the community and give back to help make it a better place.

If you have no idea where to start, you can begin by giving my friends at Smiles Change Lives a call. You can find them online at SmilesChangeLives.org to learn more about getting involved. They are a nonprofit organization located in my hometown of Kansas City. Since forming in 1997, the organization has treated more than 7,000 children. Their mission is to provide kids with life-changing orthodontic treatment when their families cannot afford the full cost of braces.

To help fund the program and meet the needs of its mission, they take donations from those in the community and hold annual events. Some of the events they hold each year include an awards night, where they recognize orthodontic providers, volunteers, and individuals who have gone above and beyond to inspire hope, raise self-esteem and help change the lives of children across the country. Each year, they also hold a Smiles Turkey Trot event, which gives people the chance to get out on Thanksgiving Day to work off some of their holiday meal and help a charity at the same time. Their Turkey Trot includes a kids' fun run, a 5K run, and a 1.5 mile walk.

STARTING A CHARITY

There are many businesses today that start their own charities. If you have a passion for something particular, especially if it's an area of orthodontics that you feel you can give back to those in your community, then starting a charity may be just the thing you should consider. Having a charity gives you the ability to be a part of something bigger than yourself and your practice, but it also supports your practice. It can be quite fulfilling to have a charity where others are being helped in the community through your efforts.

If you are interested in starting a charity, the first thing you need to do is consider what the mission will be. Who do you want to help, what will you do to help, and how will you do it? When you can answer those questions and determine what the mission is, then you are ready to move onto the next step. You need to know why you are starting a charity and what you want to get out of it. That's why it is so important to choose something you are passionate about. You will be much more willing and eager to put time into the charity if you are passionate about what you are doing with it and in fulfilling the mission.

Once you know what the mission will be, it's time to come up with a name for it. The name can be simple, or it can have deep meaning, such as my charity being named after my grandfather. If you have something sentimental you can tie to the charity name, you should do it; that helps bring meaning and purpose to your mission. Perhaps you had a favorite uncle who helped pay your way through college, so you want to honor him by naming the charity after him. Put some thought into the name and come up with something that makes sense for you.

Just like when you started your practice, you should write out a plan. Try to come up with a five-year plan so you know what you want to accomplish with the charity in the first five years. Include how you will earn funds, the types of fundraising you will engage in, how it will be operated, what the budget will look like, and more. Try to cover all of your bases here so you know what will be coming your way and can try to compensate for it.

Parents and patients who have money want to spend it with companies that make a difference.

The next stage would be to get your charity name registered. You can work with an attorney to take the legal steps to make this happen. You may also want to speak with your accountant to let them know you will be starting a charity. They can offer you information on the best ways to go about handling the money you use to get it started, as well as other advice like managing the funds and taxes.

One thing you want to keep in mind is that a registered charity needs to have an advisory board. Find people who would be a good fit for the board and put together an initial group of people. Some of the people you add to the board may have experience working with charities, so they can help you get everything started, while others may be from the dental and orthodontic community. The board may be expanded as time goes on, especially if there are large supporters whom you want to acknowledge. Board positions are always unpaid and are voluntary. If someone no longer wants to be on the board, they can be replaced by someone else interested in the position. Having an advisory board for your charity lends credibility and power and helps ensure that a variety of people are working to help the charity be successful. An advisory board should meet periodically so that everyone can keep up with what is being done and how to continue furthering the mission of the charity.

With these things in place, your next task is to set up the website and start getting your fundraising in order. Send out a press release so the newspapers and other media outlets in your area will know that the charity exists and what it is there for. Put together a plan for the first fundraising events so everyone can begin working on them. Fundraising is the key to any charity, so don't hesitate to let individuals and businesses in the community know that funds are needed in order to carry out the mission. You may just be surprised at how many people step up to offer support for what you are doing.

> *Having a charity gives you the ability to be a part of something bigger than yourself and your practice, but it also supports your practice.*

Keep good tabs on the charity and what it's doing, especially where taxes are involved. People like charities that are transparent so they know how much money is being raised and how much is going to the mission. Be sure to file taxes each year, and be patient. It takes time for a charity to get off the ground and begin fulfilling its mission. Hang in there and keep spreading the word. The community will appreciate what you are doing, and you will also end up getting referrals out of this.

As time goes on, the charity will operate more like it is on autopilot. Many of the fundraising events will be the same ones done annually, and meetings will take place on a regular basis. You can make adjustments as you go along if the board sees the changes as being beneficial for the charity as a whole. Be sure to let people know the successes of the charity and what it does to help people. When someone is helped by the charity, a fundraiser has been planned or has just finished, or other newsworthy items happen, you should always report those events to the media. Let people know you are involved in all of this great work that is helping the community.

BEING BOLD

For any charity to exist, serious fundraising needs to happen. While much of that comes from events, there are other ways of getting donations, too. You will find that there will be some major players in your community who are willing to back what you are doing. You will also find that sometimes you have to be bold to get what you require to keep that charity going and continue to help those in need in your community. I know. I've been there.

I was working on the philanthropy board for a local hospital; and after the financial collapse in 2008, we were all concerned about an upcoming drop in donations. Because of this fear, we removed the top tiers of donation requests and capped out at $10,000. One donor who had consistently given $100,000 per year failed to give at all that year. When we called and asked if he would give at the $10,000 level, he said no. When I asked him why, he said, "Because I don't think $10,000 will make a difference to anyone." So I swallowed a big gulp in my throat and asked, "Well, then, how about giving $100,000 so you know something big will happen just like last year?" He said yes and had the funds wired over the next morning.

If I had never asked him why he didn't want to give even 10 percent of what he had given in the past, I wouldn't have known how he felt. Once I heard that response, I knew that his mission was in making sure that the money he donated made a difference. That's why I went the extra step to ask him to donate more so that the mission could be carried out.

You have to be bold. But remember, you are not doing it for yourself; you are seeking those donations so you can help provide the community with something good. People who donate money want to support good being done in their community, and sometimes they just need you to be bold and say what needs to be said. All they can do in return is turn you down, so it's worth taking the chance.

Our fears had led us to believe that the most anyone would want to give during the rough economic times was $10,000. We didn't stop to consider that some people would still want to give more and would feel that the lower amount would be useless because not much could be done with it. Never underestimate the people you are asking for donations. You don't know what their plans and circumstances are, or what their mission is in being supportive of your charity.

COMMITTING TO ONE

Starting your own charity is just one possibility. You have other options as well. When you commit big to one charity, you actually get to see amazing things happen. Just like the donor who insisted on giving only at $100,000 and above, your practice should commit to something big where you are giving $25,000 or more to *one* charity so that you get the added benefit of knowing your money is going to make a difference.

If you need help finding a charity, we recommend looking at the ones that spend the majority of gifts and donations on helping the people they serve. You might be shocked to discover how much money goes to run the foundations with salaries and headquarters expenses, with only a small fraction going to the actual people in need. For a list of top charities and how much they actually give to the beneficiaries of the programs, check out www.CharityWatch.org. On this website, you will find in-depth information about a large number of charities; and the information can help you find one to donate to that you will feel proud to support. You may find it eye opening to learn that there are charity CEOs making millions per year, which means that there are millions less per year going to the causes they stand for and are soliciting donations for.

When you latch onto a big charity and start doing amazing things, don't be shy about sharing your accomplishments. Again, people want to do business with companies that make a difference. In your office tour, website, newsletters to dentists, newsletters to patients, and especially if you do a newsletter to employees only, be sure to talk about the amazing things you are doing. We even created a Burleson Cares counter that shows much we donate each year and counts up every second, matching the rate that we're donating that month. Edward Kramer said, "The hole you give through is the hole you receive through." I've found this to be particularly true in my life and in my practice.

If you can do both, starting your own charity and latching onto a big one to support, you will be doing an amazing amount of good in your community. The world is a magnet. What we send out is what comes back to us. We attract what it is that we put out into the universe. If you support others in a big way, the universe is going to support you back in a big way. That's just the way that it works. If you don't believe it, give it a try and see what happens. The more you give, the more you will tend to get back in return.

GOOD BUSINESS

One of the perks of having your own practice is that you can give to a charity of your choosing; you can select a charity that makes a connection with you. We all want things to improve in our area, whether it is regarding homelessness or helping low income kids to love their smile. By getting involved in charity, you can help make those positive changes and support such missions.

There are also a lot of perks businesses can get for donating to charities. One of the biggest perks of donating to charity is that your business will get a tax deduction. You have to pay specific attention to the rules, of course, but your business can get a tax deduction for donating to charities and also supporting charity events. So when you decide to become a sponsor of a charity's 5K, you will not only be getting your name out there in a good way by helping the causes in your community, your donations and support are also tax deductible.

Another perk from donating funds and volunteer time to charity is the free publicity you can get. Your name will be there, showing people that you give back to the community. People love to do business with companies that care about their community and help support it. Take advantage of the free publicity by putting out information regarding what you are doing for the charity. If you have a media person on your team, or if you happen to know someone who would volunteer to help raise awareness, you can send media alerts out on behalf of the event or donation. All of the publicity is a good thing and will end up bringing you some referrals.

Keep in mind that referrals are about relationships. When you align yourself with charity work, you will be strengthening many relationships with people in the community. This may be with the people you work with at the charity, or with your own patients who see that you are doing a lot of good in the community. Others who are not yet patients will also see that you are supportive of local charity missions. All of this will strengthen the relationships which will keep people referring your office, and it ties into referrals more than you may realize. While you are doing a lot of good through these charities, you will also get referrals out of it in the long run.

> *Take advantage of the free publicity by putting out information regarding what you are doing for the charity.*

Giving to charity to help support a mission will also make you happier. Research over the years has shown that people who engage in altruistic behaviors tend to be happier. They feel more personally fulfilled by doing things that help others. When you engage in altruistic behaviors, such as donating to charity, running your own charity, or volunteering for one, you will also find you have a greater sense of well-being and will feel happier. As it turns out, the more you help others be happier, the happier you become yourself.

This may possibly be one of the top reasons to help other people; you are really helping yourself, too. When you are happier in life, you are going to be better at what you do, nicer to be around, and will probably treat your patients even better. That, as you know, will translate to more referrals down the road.

By aligning yourself with a particular charity in your community, you will also be expanding your networking opportunities. It should open a whole new door to meeting new people, including some of the advisory board members who may be ideal people to network with. Just the fact that you are both involved with that particular charity gives you a common bond that will get the networking started. The basis for the relationship building is already in play. You just need to capitalize on it and see where it can lead.

In a 2013 Cone Communications Social Impact Study, they reported that 85 percent of customers are more likely to do business with a company that is associated with a charity. Consider for a moment if someone needs to see an orthodontist and they have no previous preference and are not familiar with any of those available. They go online to check out the two orthodontists they have heard of in their area and begin perusing their websites to learn more about each place. One orthodontist office does charity work to help people in the community, and one does not. Which one would they likely choose? Most of the time, people are going to choose the one that helps the charities.

If you were that person searching for a business to work with, you would also likely choose the one that gives back to charity. People like what that stands for, so be one of those companies that gives back. Give back to charity, be a part of charity, and know that it in the long run you are not only helping the charity and its mission, you are also helping your own practice with your efforts. Your office will benefit from your involvement with the charity.

TIPS FOR CHOOSING A CHARITY

In addition to logging onto the Charity Watch website to investigate the different organizations, there are some other things you will want to keep in mind as you decide which charity to align your practice with. There is nothing wrong with interviewing a charity to see if it is a good fit for you to donate your time and money to. Things you want to consider when you are reviewing charities include the following:

- **Transparency.** How much information are they giving to people, and are you comfortable with that level of transparency? You should be able to find out things like how much the charity raises each year and what amount is spent on overhead versus the program mission. If this information is nowhere to be found and they are not willing to provide it when you inquire, that is a red flag you don't want to overlook.

- **Legitimacy.** If it's a smaller charity you have not heard much about before, you should investigate to make sure they are actually a charity. Many states have online databases that make this task simple. You can log online, type in the charity name, and if they are a charity in good standing, you should be able to find information confirming that. To take a tax deduction for your donations, you will also need to confirm they are a nonprofit organization. Ask ahead of time if your donations will be tax deductible. If they say they are not tax deductible, there is a good chance they are not actually a nonprofit organization.

- **Inquire about expenses**. Since you will be making a large donation, you should find out what their expenses are and what they include. After all, your donation will help pay for those expenses. See if their CEO is making an incredibly high salary for being at a charity, or if the funds collected are largely going to support what they say they are trying to do for the community.

- **Consider the mission**. This is your time to make a difference in the community. What do you want to affect? Consider what your values are and where you would want to make an impact. This is the time to think about what area of the community you want to help, and then find a charity that has that population as its mission. Be sure you align yourself with a charity whose mission is one you can fully support. After all, your funds are going to make a difference and help them to carry that mission out. You need to feel good about what they are doing there.

- **Check their track record**. When you have your options narrowed down to a few charities, find out what their track record is. What have they accomplished up to that point? Does it seem as though they are making a difference in the community, or do they just look good online without having a record to show they have actually done much? You want to be part of a charity that has done things and has made some positive changes in the community already. Also, look beyond their own website to see what they have accomplished. Do a quick search online to see if there are other sources citing some things this charity has done such as the newspapers and television stations in your area. Look for testimonials, and see if there are other businesses in your area that are major supporters of the charity. All of this speaks volumes about their track record and where they may go in the future.

- **Ask questions.** Be sure to ask questions about the charity. If there is something you don't know or can't find the answer to online, don't hesitate to stop by to visit them, set up an appointment with their director, or give them a call to discuss it. If they provide services in your community, go and see some of their projects for yourself. You have to feel comfortable that you have all of the information you need to provide support to that charity.

The bottom line is that you want to feel good about the charity you will be giving to, and you want to make sure they are legitimate and using their funds to do what they say their mission is. When you find that, you will have found the right match for your practice. Perhaps you know of a charity right off the top of your head that you want to be a part of. If not, don't worry, there are plenty of them out there. It's just a matter of doing a little bit of research to find the right one for you.

EVENTS AND REFERRALS

Getting involved in community events that other people put on, which are separate from the ones your practice will put on, is a good way to be seen in the community. There are many events going on all year long, and some will make sense for you to support and sponsor. You can usually find some events throughout the year online, or your office may be approached by some of them as they suggest sponsorship to you. While this would be in addition to helping one big charity, it's not a bad thing to consider getting involved in. You just have to make sure that it makes sense for your practice.

Becoming an event sponsor is usually an affordable marketing opportunity. When you do it, you are also supporting a charity, because that's who usually puts them on. If you can find ways to support local charities in an affordable way, and it makes sense for your practice to align yourself with that particular cause, you may want to go for it. Sponsoring a local children's health event would make sense, for example, but sponsoring a local dog mutt strut wouldn't make much sense. By being a sponsor at the first one, your name would be a part of the marketing for that event. You would also be able to provide information to those who attend, and people in the community would see that you are a part of such things. These are opportunities to market your practice, network, and get information out and into the hands of those who need it.

It's a good idea to look into sponsoring events for charities such as the Boys & Girls Clubs, health-related events, and local PTAs. Check with your local schools to see if the PTA offers a way for you to reach out to the parents at the school. They may offer advertising opportunities on the school campus, hold events for the community, or have online advertising options. They are a charity, and parents always appreciate and support those businesses who help support the PTA. And since they operate in the schools, it makes good sense to be involved with them. They may hold charity events, such as a school health fair, where you can be a sponsor and provide information to the parents attending the event or supply fliers that will be sent home with the kids.

There are plenty of events to choose from, so whether you decide to sponsor one per year or a dozen, that's all up to you. Take a look at what's out there to see if you can find an event with a mission you can support and that makes sense for your business to be involved with. There's nothing wrong with trying it out and making adjustments. If you think it worked for you and led to some referrals, support it again the following

> The whole point about getting involved with charities and supporting their mission and some of their events is to connect with your community.

year when the event rolls around again. If you think it wasn't a good fit for your practice, then politely decline and find events and opportunities that are a better fit. Just because you try it once doesn't mean you are stuck participating forever, so don't worry about giving it a shot to test it out.

GETTING INVOLVED

The whole point about getting involved with charities and supporting their mission and some of their events is to connect with your community. As an orthodontist, you can't possibly do everything. You can't help all of the people in the community while simultaneously running your business and maintaining your sanity. But with charities around, you can reach out and do more. Getting involved with charities essentially gives you more hands to help more people. The more people you help and touch in the community, the more of them will come to know your office and what you stand for.

People appreciate those who help others and give back. They will usually choose those businesses to do business with over those who don't get involved with charities. When it comes to getting more referrals for your practice, getting involved with supporting a charity just makes sense. It will help bring more referrals over time, as well as help you create a caring image in the community. Those who see your practice as being caring and giving back to help others will appreciate it more, as well as refer it more to others. Being involved with charities is something that will not take much of your time, but it will pay off well in the long run.

CHAPTER TWENTY

EVERYONE IS IN THE REFERRAL BUSINESS

You have made it this far, which means you now know a lot more about referrals than when you began this book. Of course there is always something more to learn, but this book puts you on solid footing to start your referral program, maintain it, and grow your practice. By putting to use the information in this book, you can create a successful referral system that will not only sustain your practice, but help it thrive for years to come. I have used this referral system for years, so I know it is a proven method that will work when put into action.

I want to mention books and how important they are in helping you to grow your practice and reach the level of success you are seeking. I'm a firm believer that books shouldn't be left stacked on a shelf, their pages showing little or no wear. If you browse through my library of over 3,000 books on display (there are more in storage) you will find notes, dog eared pages, and scribbles in the margins. Some books may even have only the important pages cut out and stuffed back inside the dust jacket with the rest of the book having been thrown out. You will see action items on the side cover with the initial date of reading, my name, and the dates I reread it, along with the review notes and page numbers of interest.

I'm never at a loss for ideas for team trainings or newsletter articles. I have tens of thousands of notes scribbled inside my books, and it is with that spirit that I'm going to encourage you to scribble inside this book. Below each of the review points from the book, you will find reference notes, articles, and suggested additional reading.

In my career, I've discovered if I look up the thought leaders on any given topic—such as referrals—and then I read their books or articles and look up the references in the back of those books and articles, within two or three layers, I've covered the entire body of literature and research on a particular topic. The curiosity to look up the references, read them, and search their references will give you 98 percent of the knowledge base in any area of life. The library is your friend. Stop digging only at the surface in your search for knowledge. Go broad and go much deeper.

We now live in a time when there are over 1 million books being published each year. That's a lot of information. Not all of it will be of good quality; but if you take the time to seek out the good quality books on business, building relationships, marketing, and more, you will gain a ton of information and ideas that you can put to use in your practice.

Below you will find a breakdown of each of the previous chapters with additional information. Use this to delve deeper and grow higher.

CHAPTER 1

Referrals are gold in the dental field, but many people don't have the time to give referrals. This goes for both patients and other dentists in your area. Why? There are several reasons for that, including that they assume you are already busy enough and that they don't find the image you display overly inviting.

Most orthodontists I've worked with report that they get most of their new patients through word-of-mouth routes, not realizing *that* is how referrals work. Patients need to see you in situations and environments where you're not always busy and providing treatment. They need to know you are a real person with whom they can talk and laugh. This image of always being busy and only seeing people at the office can hold you back from getting referrals.

People also need to know that the quality of your service will not drop if they begin to send more people your way and you become busier. Maintaining high quality service and offering ease of availability will always be important to people who consider referring your office to others. Patients, dentists, hygienists, and others need to see you outside the office at times so they can lay the foundation for building a relationship. Referrals happen as a result of those relationships you build with those around you. It's important to get out and engage in the community through events so people can see another side of you and get to know you.

Action Item

Make a list of at least five events you can attend in the coming year that will give you an opportunity to mingle with people in the community, especially your patients and area dental professionals.

1. _____

2. _____

3. _____

4. _____

5. _____

Additional reading

"Ten Ways to Strengthen Referral Relationships" by Ivan Misner, *Entrepreneur Magazine*, 2011.

CHAPTER 2

People often don't know *how* to refer someone to your office. Most are not equipped to make a good quality referral. It is your job to make sure your patients have tools to make it easier for them to refer people to you. There are numerous options when it comes to the types of tools you can have, including brochures, online posts where they can tag friends, email newsletters that are easy to forward, and books. When they have the tools they need, they are more likely to make the referral. Newsletters and social media can be useful tools in your referral system if they are used properly. Create a rewards program that will encourage people who send you referrals. Even if you send them a gift certificate for lunch at a nearby restaurant, you will entice them to want to send more referrals. People who send you business should be rewarded for their efforts, but always avoid engaging in practices that may seem shady when it comes to getting reviews or "likes" on your social media pages. Purchasing fake reviews or likes leaves a lot to be desired and can call into question the integrity of your practice. Only take those reviews and likes that you have legitimately earned. If you do happen to get negative reviews or comments, don't ignore them. It's best to address them right away, so the person with the complaint and others can see that you are attempting to rectify the situation.

Action item:

Make a list of five tools you can offer patients to help them refer your office.

1. _____

2. _____

3. _____

4. _____

5. _____

Additional reading:

"52 Types of Marketing Strategies" by BJ Bueno and Scott Jeffrey, *The Cult Branding Company*, 2013.

CHAPTER 3

One of the big reasons people don't give out referrals is because they are only getting an adequate experience themselves. If your patients are just getting what is expected and you are not going above and beyond for them, then there's not a lot of reason for them to refer you. They expect adequate treatment coming to your office. If they get just that, it is unlikely you will get referrals. If you go above that and are exceptional, then you will get referrals. People don't refer adequate or acceptable: they refer above average and exceptional. People do not talk about boring things: they talk about things that are interesting and great, things that "wow" them. Good customer service has largely faded in today's consumer world, so if you provide it, you will stand out. Your entire team needs to be on board with providing excellent service; and they need to know how to go about doing so, even if they have to be trained in order to do it. Your patients need to know that you appreciate them and that you care about them. Even the small things, such as using manners with them, will go a long way. Wow patients with things like birthday notes, small gifts, and remembering that they love the New York Yankees (or whatever their thing may be). Strive to be extraordinary.

Action item:

Name three areas of your patient experience you can honestly say are "adequate," but not exceptional. What can you do to change them?

1. _____

2. _____

3. _____

Additional reading:

The Zappos Experience: 5 Principles to Inspire, Engage, and WOW by Joseph Michelli

The Starbucks Experience: 5 Principles for Turning Ordinary into Extraordinary by Joseph Michelli

CHAPTER 4

When you get new patients in your office, what do you do to welcome them? If you are like most orthodontists, it's not a whole lot. But it should be. If you want to be exceptional you need to impress your patients from the moment they make contact with your office. Every new patient you get should be welcomed in a *big* way. Whether you do this with a handwritten note and Starbucks gift card, or something else, you should be doing it. They need to feel acknowledged and appreciated for choosing you, rather than just being another patient on a long list. Lack of individual attention is a major problem in today's business world. People are willing to pay more for personalized attention, and you don't have to spend a fortune to make that happen. Rather than putting all of the focus on you and advancing your career, turn your focus to your patients and what you can do to make their experience better right from the start. If people are not welcomed to your practice in a big way, they will not feel appreciated or special and will never want to refer you to their friends and family. Wow them right from the start by letting them know you notice them and appreciate them coming to your office, and they will want to refer you to others. It's a small shift in the way your new patients are handled, but it can have a major impact on referrals for years to come.

Action item:

List five things you can do to welcome patients in a big way.

1. _____

2. _____

3. _____

4. _____

5. _____

Additional reading:

"Win Their Loyalty: Ensure Your Customers Feel Special" by Alana Muller, *Forbes Magazine*, 2012.

CHAPTER 5

If you referred one of your friends to someone and never got a thank-you or shred of gratitude from the company, would you refer more people to them? Probably not. I find that many orthodontists don't take the time to give thanks and show appreciation for the referrals they get, but it's important to always give proper thanks. This goes both to your patients who are referring your office and to those referring dentists who are sending people your way. Take the time to thank them promptly and show that you appreciate their referrals. Think of every referral you get as a gift, which is exactly what it is. If someone gives you a gift, don't you feel the urge to show them some gratitude and thank them for thinking of you? Of course you do. Yet so many people pass up the opportunity to give thanks for the referrals that they get. When you give thanks for every referral you receive, people will know that you appreciate that they sent someone your way, and they will feel good about doing it again. Ideally, you should have a plan for how to thank every new referral that comes in and to make your referral sources feel special. This can include sending them handwritten thank-you notes, surprising your top referral sources with some professional basketball tickets, or having referral VIP parties where your top referring sources are invited. Whether you keep it simple or you have a more elaborate plan, always have a plan in place for showing gratitude for every new referral.

Action item:

List five things you can do to show your referral sources gratitude and to thank them.

1. _____

2. _____

3. _____

4. _____

5. _____

Additional reading:

"10 Ways to Say 'Thank You'" by Kara Ohngren Prior, *Entrepreneur Magazine,* 2016.

CHAPTER 6

I have consulted orthodontists around the world and have heard time and again that they don't even have a referral system in place. Most businesses don't have one in place, which is a huge mistake. Being a great orthodontist is not all it takes to bring people in the door: people have to know about you. Either you can spend a lot of money marketing yourself, or you can build relationships and get referrals. I much prefer the latter, and I hope you do, too. You know that referrals are important, but what are you doing right now to get them each month? It's time to get serious about tracking your marketing expenses to see where the money is going and what the cost per referral is, so you know if it's worth the effort. You also need to let your patients and area dentists know that you want referrals. They may not even realize that you are seeking referrals. It is also important to have a guarantee, so you can set yourself apart from your competition. Every month, you have to make efforts to get new referrals; and you need to track them so you know where your new patients are coming from and what the cost per referral is. You will repeat those efforts monthly in order to keep the referrals coming in on steady basis. Remember, you need to be anything but boring. Vanilla only works with ice cream.

Action items:

List five things you can do each month to stimulate new referrals.

1. _____

2. _____

3. _____

4. _____

5. _____

List three places you are spending marketing money and how many referrals come from it each month.

1. _____

2. _____

3. _____

Additional reading:

"One Simple Metric You Need to Determine Marketing ROI" by Victor Ho, *Inc. Magazine,* 2013.

CHAPTER 7

There are many strategies you can use as part of your referral system. You can do them all or you can pick and choose the ones that you prefer. I try to incorporate doing them all to some degree because I'm always in referral thinking mode—and you should be, too. An important strategy for your office is to host several big events throughout the year, which only your VIP referral sources are invited to attend. Make it fun, memorable, and tailored so it makes them feel special. They will want to keep on referring your office and attending those parties. You can also hold monthly referral contests (giving away prizes to the top referral sources), offer patient newsletters, have in-office signage, and send patient surveys and email automation campaigns. Additionally, consider doing something outrageous once in a while to get some "forced" referrals. This is where you have done something so exceptional that people just feel they *have* to talk about you and your office. You may already be doing some of these things, or none at all. It's important to plan which ones you will do so you know they are being done each month. Consistently doing them will keep the referrals coming in on a regular basis.

Action item:
List five strategies you can start doing immediately to encourage referrals.

1. _____

2. _____

3. _____

4. _____

5. _____

Additional reading:
"How to Host an Event for a Small Business" by Kaleigh Moore, *Grasshopper,* 2014.

CHAPTER 8

To have a successful referral system, you need to be aware of your timing and strategy. It really does matter when you send out that referral and ask for more. It's important to contact your referral sources promptly when you receive a new referral, rather than put it off. Being busy is a catch-all phrase these days and one that will keep you from getting more referrals. Never be too busy to follow up with those sending you referrals. Don't be a slacker, either, by sending canned and automated responses. People can tell how insincere that is and won't feel appreciated. Opt for handwritten messages that may take a little longer, but will be seen as a true sign of gratitude. Also, stop going after one referral when you are likely to get many more than that from each referral source. Apply the 80/20 rule to determine how many referring patients you have. Chances are, about 80 percent of your business is being referred to you by 20 percent of your patients. Within that 20 percent, you will have people who have referred you multiple times. Those people make up your VIP list and should be treated like VIPs. Empower your employees do follow up on your behalf so that it is always done promptly. Remember, consumers by and large trust word-of-mouth referrals above all else. Be mindful of these things as you create a plan for your referral strategy system and you will be ahead of the game and keep those referrals coming in at a steady pace.

Action item:

Identify and make a list of your top five referral sources. These are the top of your VIPs.

1. _____

2. _____

3. _____

4. _____

5. _____

Additional reading:

"What are the Benefits of Employee Empowerment?"
by Leigh Richards, *The Houston Chronicle*, 2016.

CHAPTER 9

Most orthodontists overlook the importance of internal marketing. Take a look around your office at your team: every one of them is a force for bringing in referrals, and they can help your office bring in plenty of them. They can also be the one thing that keeps you from getting referrals if they have poor attitudes and bad customer service skills. With the right people on your team, you will have a referral force that will drive your practice further into success. Now is the time to consider what your referral system life cycle would look like if you devised your dream plan. There is a best time to ask for referrals, and that happens to be the moment the braces come off. Aim to lengthen that feel good time and ask for referrals when they are feeling great about the treatment. Always aim for long-lasting successful referral sources over ones that will only provide instant gratification. Pay attention to what others do to get referrals, but don't obsess over it. If you have the chance to pick a few brains for ideas, take it, because you never know what you may learn along the way.

Action item:

Write what your dream referral system life cycle would look like.

_____

_____

_____

_____

List three people you'd like to chat with for ideas (or, "pick their brain").

1. _____

2. _____

3. _____

This week, call at least one of them and ask them to meet for coffee or lunch. Let the picking begin.

Additional reading:

"7 Rules of a Successful Business Lunch" by Matthew Swyers, _Inc. Magazine_, 2012.

CHAPTER 10

Most orthodontists do not keep track of their referral efforts to see if what they are doing works or could use an overhaul. If you don't measure what you are doing, then there's a good chance you won't know if you are moving toward success and making progress or not. I always recommend that people track what they are doing, including the time and costs involved, and then analyze to see which of their efforts is worth repeating. It is also important to diversify your referral sources. Getting all of your referrals from just one or two sources, as some people do, can be disastrous for your practice if something changes and those referrals slow up or cease all together. Keep in mind that not all referrals are equal. Some are going to be more valuable to your practice than others. It is your job to find out which type is more valuable and what to do to bring more of those in the door. Be sure to also pay attention to patient retention. It is costly to replace lost patients. Fix what may be prompting patients to leave, rather than continue to pay the high cost of replacing them.

Action item:

What two things can you identify in your office that may be prompting patients to leave?

1. _____

2. _____

List three local dentists you get the most referrals from.

1. _____

2. _____

3. _____

Additional reading:

"How to Diversify Your Customer Base" by Tara Miller, *Inc. Magazine*, 2010.

CHAPTER 11

Having a practical and professional referral system strategy is just good business. Yet most doctors do not take the time to think through one or act on putting one into action. Had you thought about a referral system prior to picking up this book? If you are like most orthodontists, you did not. That's because they don't understand the potential benefits of having one, such as cutting lead time in half for every referral you get or even reducing your marketing expenditure by at least half when you have a successful referral system in place. Keep in mind that people refer to those they trust—this goes for dentist and patients alike. Don't be held back from creating a referral system by a fear of failure, and always do damage control when it's needed so you can maintain the trust that you have earned, and that can easily be taken away. Testimonials can be an important tool in your referral system.

Action item:

Make a list of five people you can immediately ask for a written testimonial.

1. _____

2. _____

3. _____

4. _____

5. _____

Additional reading:

"How to Effectively Use Testimonials" by Derek Gehl, *Entrepreneur Magazine,* 2016.

CHAPTER 12

As an orthodontist, it is crucial to build good relationships with the dentists in your area. Take a drive around your city and see how many dentists you have not yet stopped to meet. Each of them is a potential gold mine for your practice. Many will send you referrals just from your stopping in, introducing yourself, and asking for the referrals. It is important that you network with others in your field, and those relationships you build with local dentists are the building blocks of the repeat business that we do. Keep in mind that when you help others succeed, you will also succeed. There's nothing wrong with building a two-way street with others in your area; in fact, it is a smart move. Once you have numerous dentists who trust you enough to send you their patients, be sure to do everything you can to keep them happy. Show them gratitude, provide them with the information they need about the patients' treatment progress, and do things to strengthen that relationship.

Action item:

List 10 dentists in your area who are *not* referring to you yet.

1. _____

2. _____

3. _____

4. _____

5. _____

6. _____

7. _____

8. _____

9. _____

10. _____

Next, invite each of them to a lunch and learn, where you will provide info about what sets you apart. Be sure to have the lunch catered, offer prizes, and make it a fun and memorable experience. Speak with each of the people who attend so you can begin to build a relationship with them.

Additional reading:

"3 Keys to a Successful Lunch & Learn" *MSPmentor,* 2015.

CHAPTER 13

Nearly all the orthodontists I have consulted believed that the only doctors they could get referrals from were local dentists. Yet there are so many more beyond that. Look beyond the dentists in your area to a whole new world of doctors that are each potential referral sources. You want to make a connection with those in your area that are pediatricians, ENTs, family practitioners, allergists, plastic surgeons, and neurologists. You have something to offer each of their patients. Let them know this by making a connection with them and providing them the right tools. The information and tools you provide them should be relevant to their patients' needs. Also, keep track of all the contacts you make with these doctors. You can do so by using a customer relationship management (CRM) software program. Continue to plant seeds with all of the doctors in your area. You never know when one of their patients will need an orthodontist; but when they do, you want to be the one they think of for the referral. Building relationships with each of these doctors puts you in the prime position to be the one they think of first.

Action item:

List five doctors in your area you can immediately reach out to and make a connection.

1. _____

2. _____

3. _____

4. _____

5. _____

Additional reading:

Best CRM Software 2017 by Sara Angeles, *Business News Daily,* 2017.

CHAPTER 14

When we look even beyond other area doctors, we can see that there are other medical professionals who can be solid referral sources. It is important to cast a wide net to have a large pool of places and types of places that are sending you referrals. You never want all your eggs in one basket. Don't let the fact that you may not understand everything about their specialty keep you away. You don't have to know everything, just as they don't have to know everything about orthodontics. Try to pick up some of the basics, so you are aware of some of the more common issues you could help with and some of the terminology. It's important to have a back-up system in place so you always know what you are doing for plan A and plan B. Prioritize your referral sources, identifying those that have the best potential, so you can maximize your efforts to build relationships with those sources. Always remember the staff at places you work with, too, as they often have the first opportunity to provide patients with referrals and recommendations.

Action item:

List five medical specialists you can immediately reach out to and make a connection.

1. _____

2. _____

3. _____

4. _____

5. _____

Additional reading:

"8 Tips to Building a Strong Referral Relationship" *Data Soft Logic,* 2016.

CHAPTER 15

The more you look around, the more you will see that there are many referral opportunities. Even around your office, there are businesses that you can collaborate with in order to send each other business. It is in your best interest to contact these places in order to find a way to work together, such as offering their customers a discount card. You will need to work your way up the ladder to have a chance to speak with the person who holds the power to make such decisions, but if you try you can make it happen. It is important to get to know your neighbors so you can work with those businesses, regardless of what type they are. If you do not, then you are leaving money on the table. Small-business networking is a good way to bring in more referrals. Consider collaborating with in such places as medical spas and taking part in health fairs and other community events that make sense to do so. This is all about casting your net wider. Tailor your message or offer to your specific audience, but make connections with those around you and get involved where it makes sense to do so.

Action item:

List five businesses near your office you can begin contacting regarding collaboration.

1. _____

2. _____

3. _____

4. _____

5. _____

Additional reading:

"3 Tips for Hosting Company Events with Strong ROI" *Hootsuite*, 2014.

CHAPTER 16

If you want to have a lot of referrals, you will have to get into the habit of attending, sponsoring and throwing events. The events are important because they get people excited, and that gets them talking about your office. There are no limits to the type of events you can get involved in. Consider the many events that will go on in your community this year and see which ones make sense for you to be involved in. You should also organize your own events throughout the year and invite your VIPs to them. Make sure you are anything but boring, so that people leave there with a reason to talk about your office.

Action item:

List five events you can be involved in this year.

1. _____

2. _____

3. _____

4. _____

5. _____

Additional reading:

Festival Planning Guide: Creating Community Events with Big Hearts and Small Budgets by Betty Lucke

CHAPTER 17

Having a referral system in place takes time, and it may not be something that you want to take on completely. The good news is that it is a job that you can delegate or hire someone for, but it is important to make sure you have the right person filling that position. They need to be personable, so you want to choose someone based more on their attitude than anything else. Discuss the goals with them of what you would like the end result to be, but give them some space to do the work using their own style and resources. Start out with providing them with a list of 10 places you would like to start getting referrals from. Check in with them to see if there is anything they need and evaluate periodically to see if goals are being met. Don't fear delegation, because it's something that all good leaders do. Never stop prospecting.

Action item:

List 10 places you would like to start getting referrals from.

1. _____

2. _____

3. _____

4. _____

5. _____

6. _____

7. _____

8. _____

9. _____

10. _____

Additional reading:

"7 Tips to Help You Delegate More Effectively" by Peter Economy, *Inc. Magazine,* 2014.

CHAPTER 18

The new generation of employees that many of us are working with today is different than prior ones in that they value experiences more than they value money. This means that if you want to give employee incentives, you should consider things beyond that, such as the enabling them to master something, giving them autonomy, and creating a sense of purpose. It is good for your office to help your employees learn to master something they are interested in, whether that is quilting or mountain climbing. When they can master something they become happier people, and happier people make for better and more productive employees. Give your employees time each year to put volunteer hours into the community. This will help your community and will help the person to feel good about the fact that they have a sense of purpose. We are happier people when we help others and are involved in something bigger than ourselves. Support their getting involved and giving back. There are many companies doing this today because there are so many benefits that come from it. It's easy to do, promotes good will, and brings good back to you.

Action item:

Write a list of five places where you would like to support your employees to volunteer.

1. _____

2. _____

3. _____

4. _____

5. _____

Additional reading:

"Gen Z Employees: The 5 Attributes You Need to Know" by Dan Schawbel, *Entrepreneur Magazine,* 2014.

CHAPTER 19

Every practice should choose one charity to support, and do so in a big way. Make the commitment to one charity that you will give a lot of money to over the year. Be bold so that it actually helps to make a difference in your community. When choosing a charity to support, be sure to get one that is rated well, so your money gets put to good use. You can also consider starting your own charity, as I have done, and get other people to support it and your mission. Having a charity of your own gives you a chance to do a lot of good in the community and give back to a cause that is close to your heart. Be sure to follow the rules for establishing a charity of your own, so that everything is legitimate and recognized by the IRS. It's not as difficult as you may think, and it can do a lot to help your practice make a great connection with the community.

Action item:

Write down what your ideal charity would be if you were to start your own.

_____

_____

_____

_____

Additional reading:

Start Something That Matters by Blake Mycoskie

FINAL THOUGHTS

Having a successful referral system is something that I have done and you can do, too. It takes time, dedication, and effective management in order for it to be successful. Within the pages of this book, you have learned my insider tips for how to get it started, the many things that matter and what to look for, and how to keep your practice growing. You can have a continuous stream of referrals. But first you have to put these things into action, make the commitment to keep at it, and then be patient. In time, the referrals will flow and your business will grow.

About the Author

DR. DUSTIN S. BURLESON IS a speaker, teacher, author and business strategist for thousands of doctors located in 25 countries throughout the world. He writes and edits four newsletters monthly, is the director of the Rheam Foundation for Cleft & Craniofacial Orthodontics and operates a large multi-doctor, multi-clinic orthodontic and pediatric dental practice in Kansas City, Missouri. He is a champion of the private practitioner and has a long track record of helping orthodontists transform their practices and increase their impact on their families, employees, communities and the profession of orthodontics. His orthodontic marketing campaigns have generated over $425 million in revenue for his clients and privately-held practices.

When he is not working, you can find him on his sailboat, jumping out of airplanes, or racing exotic cars through the desert. In a tightly-contested vote, he was recently named Best Dad in the World by two-thirds of his children.

VISIT **TheReferralsBook.com** TO ACCESS THESE FREE RESOURCES:

 **RECEIVE** a free audio disc where Dr. Burleson shares his best internal marketing campaigns and event-based marketing ideas to help you grow your orthodontic practice.

 **REGISTER** for a complimentary on-line training event led by Dr. Burleson, "How to Convert 90% or More of Your New Patients into Starting Treatment Without the Gimmicks or Hype & Without Turning Your Treatment Coordinators into Used Car Salesmen Even if EVERYTHING YOU'VE TRIED Up Until Now Hasn't Worked..."

 **COMPLETE** the Burleson Challenge and see if your practice qualifies to join one of Dustin's private coaching groups where you will work directly with many of the top orthodontists throughout the world and quickly determine the next steps required to take your practice to the next level.

ACCESS ALL OF THE ABOVE FREE RESOURCES
BY REGISTERING YOUR BOOK AT

TheReferralsBook.com

73722509R00141

Made in the USA
Columbia, SC
16 July 2017